2018 SQA Specimen and Past Papers with Answers

Higher
HUMAN BIOLOGY

2017 & 2018 Exams
and 2018 Specimen Question Paper

HODDER
GIBSON
AN HACHETTE UK COMPANY

This book contains the official SQA 2017 and 2018 Exams, and the 2018 Specimen Question Paper for Higher Human Biology, with associated SQA-approved answers modified from the official marking instructions that accompany the paper.

In addition the book contains study skills advice. This advice has been specially commissioned by Hodder Gibson, and has been written by experienced senior teachers and examiners in line with the new Higher syllabus and assessment outlines. This is not SQA material but has been devised to provide further guidance for Higher examinations.

Hodder Gibson is grateful to the copyright holders, as credited on the final page of the Answer section, for permission to use their material. Every effort has been made to trace the copyright holders and to obtain their permission for the use of copyright material. Hodder Gibson will be happy to receive information allowing us to rectify any error or omission in future editions.

Hachette UK's policy is to use papers that are natural, renewable and recyclable products and made from wood grown in sustainable forests. The logging and manufacturing processes are expected to conform to the environmental regulations of the country of origin.

Orders: please contact Bookpoint Ltd, 130 Park Drive, Milton Park, Abingdon, Oxon OX14 4SE. Telephone: (44) 01235 827827. Fax: (44) 01235 400454. Lines are open 9.00–5.00, Monday to Saturday, with a 24-hour message answering service. Visit our website at www.hoddereducation.co.uk. Hodder Gibson can also be contacted directly at hoddergibson@hodder.co.uk

This collection first published in 2018 by
Hodder Gibson, an imprint of Hodder Education,
An Hachette UK Company
211 St Vincent Street
Glasgow G2 5QY

Typeset by Aptara, Inc.

Printed in the UK

A catalogue record for this title is available from the British Library

ISBN: 978-1-5104-5667-9

2 1

2019 2018

MIX
Paper from
responsible sources
FSC™ C104740
FSC
www.fsc.org

Introduction

Higher Human Biology

The practice papers in this book give you an overall and comprehensive coverage of assessment of **Knowledge** and **Skills of Scientific Inquiry** for the Higher Human Biology.

We recommend that you refer to Higher Human Biology Course Specification pages 36–87 from the SQA website at www.sqa.org.uk/sqa/47915.html This document tells you what will be tested in your examination. You should note that both the Key Area and Depth of Knowledge columns can be examined. It is expected that you be familiar with the apparatus and techniques detailed on page 87.

The course

The Higher Human Biology Course consists of three areas of Human Biology. These are human cells, physiology and health, and neurobiology and immunology. In each area, you will be assessed on your ability to demonstrate and apply knowledge of Human Biology and to demonstrate and apply skills of scientific inquiry. Candidates must also complete an Assignment in which they research a topic in human biology and write it up as a report. They also take a Course examination.

How the course is graded

The grade you achieve for Higher Human Biology depends on the following two course assessments, which are set and graded by SQA.

1. A report based on an Assignment, which is worth 20% of the grade. The Assignment is marked out of 20 marks which is then scaled to 30 marks.

2. A written course examination is worth the remaining 80% of the grade. The examination is marked out of 120 marks, most of which are for the demonstration and application of knowledge although there are also marks available for skills of scientific inquiry.

This book should help you practise the examination part! To pass Higher Human Biology with a C grade you will need about 50% of the 150 marks available for the Assignment and the Course Examination combined. For a B you will need roughly 60% and, for an A, roughly 70%.

The course examination

The Course Examination consists of two Papers.

- **Paper 1** is an objective test with 25 multiple-choice items for 25 marks.
- **Paper 2** is a mix of restricted and extended-response questions worth between 1 and 10 marks each for a total of 95 marks. The majority of the marks test knowledge with an emphasis on the application of knowledge. The remainder test the application of scientific inquiry, analysis and problem solving skills. There will always be a large experimental question and a large data handling question worth between 5 and 9 marks each. There will be two or three extended-response questions worth between 10 and 15 marks in total. At least one of the extended-response questions will include a choice of topic.

Altogether, there are 120 marks and you will have 40 minutes to complete Paper 1, a 30 minute break followed by 2 hours and 20 minutes to complete Paper 2. The majority of the marks will be straightforward and linked to grade C but about 30% of the marks are more demanding and are linked to grade A.

General tips and hints

Each paper in this book can be attempted in its entirety or groups of questions on a particular topic or skill area can be attempted. If you are trying a whole examination paper from this book, give yourself 2 hours and 30 minutes maximum to complete either the 2017 or 2018 Papers and allow 3 hours for the Specimen Paper. Make sure that you spend time in using the answer section to mark your own work – it is especially useful if you can get someone to help you with this.

The marking instructions give acceptable answers with alternatives. You could even grade your work on an A–D basis. The following hints and tips are related to examination techniques as well as avoiding common mistakes. Remember that if you hit problems with a question, you should ask your teacher for help.

Paper 1

25 multiple-choice items   25 marks

- Answer on the grid.
- You are allocated 40 minutes to complete this Paper.
- Some individual questions might take longer to answer than others – this is quite normal and make sure you use scrap paper if a calculation or any working is needed.
- Some questions can be answered instantly – again, this is normal.
- Do not leave blanks – complete the grid for each question as you work through.
- Try to answer each question in your head without looking at the options. If your answer is there you are home and dry!
- If you are not certain, choose the answer that seemed most attractive on first reading the answer options.
- If you are guessing, try to eliminate options before making your guess. If you can eliminate three – you are left with the correct answer even if you do not recognise it!

Paper 2

Restricted and extended-response questions   95 marks

- You are allocated 2 hours and 20 minutes for this Paper.
- Answer on the question paper. Try to write neatly and keep your answers on the support lines if possible – the lines are designed to take the full answer!
- A clue to answer length is the mark allocation – most questions are restricted to 1 mark and the answer can be quite short. If there are 2–4 marks available, your answer will need to be extended and may well have two, three or even four parts.
- Questions are designed to test the content within a key area but some questions are integrated and may contain content from more than one key area.
- The C-type questions usually start with "State", "Identify", "Give" or "Name" and often need only a word or two in response. They will usually be for 1 mark each.
- Questions that begin with "Explain", "Describe" or "Suggest" are usually A-types and are likely to have more than one part to the full answer. You will usually have to write a sentence or two and there may be 2 or even 3 marks available.
- Make sure you read questions over twice before trying to answer – there is often very important information within the question and you are unlikely to be short of time in this examination.

- Using abbreviations like DNA and ATP is fine and the bases of DNA can be given as A, T, G and C. The Higher Human Biology Course Specification will give you the acceptable abbreviations.
- Don't worry that a few questions are in unfamiliar contexts, that's the idea! Just keep calm and read the questions carefully.
- If a question contains a choice, be sure to spend a minute or two making the best choice for you.
- In experimental questions, you must be aware of what variables are, why controls are needed and how reliability and validity might be improved. It is worth spending time on these ideas – they are essential and will come up year after year.
- Some candidates like to use a highlighter pen to help them focus on the essential points of longer questions – this is a great technique.
- Remember that a conclusion can be seen from data, whereas an explanation will usually require you to supply some background knowledge as well.
- If you are asked to draw a conclusion, make sure you relate it to any aim stated in the question.
- Remember to use values and units from the graph when describing graphical information in words if you are asked to do so.
- Plot graphs carefully and join the plot points using a ruler. Include zeros on your scale where appropriate and use the data table headings for the axes labels.
- Look out for graphs with two Y-axes – these need extra special concentration and anyone can make a mistake!
- If there is a space for calculation given – you will very likely need to use it! A calculator is essential.
- The main types of calculation tend to be ratios, averages, percentages and percentage change – make sure you can do these common calculations.
- Answers to calculations will not usually have more than two decimal places.
- Give units in calculation answers if they are not already given in the answer space.
- Do not leave blanks. Always have a go, using the language in the question if you can.

Good luck!

Remember that the rewards for passing Higher Human Biology are well worth it! Your pass will help you get the future you want for yourself. In the exam, be confident in your own ability. If you're not sure how to answer a question, trust your instincts and just give it a go anyway.

Keep calm and don't panic! GOOD LUCK!

Study Skills – what you need to know to pass exams!

General exam revision: 20 top tips

When preparing for exams, it is easy to feel unsure of where to start or how to revise. This guide to general exam revision provides a good starting place, and, as these are very general tips, they can be applied to all your exams.

1. Start revising in good time.

Don't leave revision until the last minute – this will make you panic and it will be difficult to learn. Make a revision timetable that counts down the weeks to go.

2. Work to a study plan.

Set up sessions of work spread through the weeks ahead. Make sure each session has a focus and a clear purpose. What will you study, when and why? Be realistic about what you can achieve in each session, and don't be afraid to adjust your plans as needed.

3. Make sure you know exactly when your exams are.

Get your exam dates from the SQA website and use the timetable builder tool to create your own exam schedule. You will also get a personalised timetable from your school, but this might not be until close to the exam period.

4. Make sure that you know the topics that make up each course.

Studying is easier if material is in manageable chunks – why not use the SQA topic headings or create your own from your class notes? Ask your teacher for help on this if you are not sure.

5. Break the chunks up into even smaller bits.

The small chunks should be easier to cope with. Remember that they fit together to make larger ideas. Even the process of chunking down will help!

6. Ask yourself these key questions for each course:

- Are all topics compulsory or are there choices?
- Which topics seem to come up time and time again?
- Which topics are your strongest and which are your weakest?

Use your answers to these questions to work out how much time you will need to spend revising each topic.

7. Make sure you know what to expect in the exam.

The subject-specific introduction to this book will help with this. Make sure you can answer these questions:

- How is the paper structured?
- How much time is there for each part of the exam?
- What types of question are involved? These will vary depending on the subject so read the subject-specific section carefully.

8. Past papers are a vital revision tool!

Use past papers to support your revision wherever possible. This book contains the answers and mark schemes too – refer to these carefully when checking your work. Using the mark scheme is useful; even if you don't manage to get all the marks available first time when you first practise, it helps you identify how to extend and develop your answers to get more marks next time – and of course, in the real exam.

9. Use study methods that work well for you.

People study and learn in different ways. Reading and looking at diagrams suits some students. Others prefer to listen and hear material – what about reading out loud or getting a friend or family member to do this for you? You could also record and play back material.

10. There are three tried and tested ways to make material stick in your long-term memory:

- Practising – e.g. rehearsal, repeating
- Organising – e.g. making drawings, lists, diagrams, tables, memory aids
- Elaborating – e.g. incorporating the material into a story or an imagined journey

11. Learn actively.

Most people prefer to learn actively – for example, making notes, highlighting, redrawing and redrafting, making up memory aids, or writing past paper answers. A good way to stay engaged and inspired is to mix and match these methods – find the combination that best suits you. This is likely to vary depending on the topic or subject.

12. Be an expert.

Be sure to have a few areas in which you feel you are an expert. This often works because at least some of them will come up, which can boost confidence.

13. Try some visual methods.

Use symbols, diagrams, charts, flashcards, post-it notes etc. Don't forget – the brain takes in chunked images more easily than loads of text.

14. Remember – practice makes perfect.

Work on difficult areas again and again. Look and read – then test yourself. You cannot do this too much.

15. Try past papers against the clock.

Practise writing answers in a set time. This is a good habit from the start but is especially important when you get closer to exam time.

16. Collaborate with friends.

Test each other and talk about the material – this can really help. Two brains are better than one! It is amazing how talking about a problem can help you solve it.

17. Know your weaknesses.

Ask your teacher for help to identify what you don't know. Try to do this as early as possible. If you are having trouble, it is probably with a difficult topic, so your teacher will already be aware of this – most students will find it tough.

18. Have your materials organised and ready.

Know what is needed for each exam:

- Do you need a calculator or a ruler?
- Should you have pencils as well as pens?
- Will you need water or paper tissues?

19. Make full use of school resources.

Find out what support is on offer:

- Are there study classes available?
- When is the library open?
- When is the best time to ask for extra help?
- Can you borrow textbooks, study guides, past papers, etc.?
- Is school open for Easter revision?

20. Keep fit and healthy!

Try to stick to a routine as much as possible, including with sleep. If you are tired, sluggish or dehydrated, it is difficult to see how concentration is even possible. Combine study with relaxation, drink plenty of water, eat sensibly, and get fresh air and exercise – all these things will help more than you could imagine. Good luck!

HIGHER

2017

National Qualifications 2017

X740/76/02

Human Biology
Section 1 — Questions

TUESDAY, 23 MAY

1:00 PM — 3:30 PM

Instructions for the completion of Section 1 are given on *Page two* of your question and answer booklet X740/76/01.

Record your answers on the answer grid on *Page three* of your question and answer booklet.

Before leaving the examination room you must give your question and answer booklet to the Invigilator; if you do not, you may lose all the marks for this paper.

SECTION 1 — 20 marks

Attempt ALL questions

1. Which row in the table shows the type of stem cell that has the potential to form the greatest variety of specialised cells?

	Type of stem cell	State of differentiation
A	embryonic	differentiated
B	tissue	differentiated
C	embryonic	undifferentiated
D	tissue	undifferentiated

2. The graph contains information about prostate cancer in the UK in 2006.

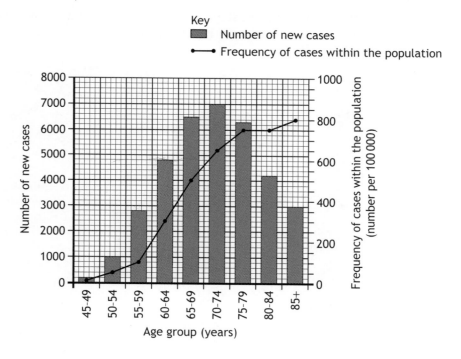

Key

▓ Number of new cases

●—● Frequency of cases within the population

Which of the following conclusions can be drawn from the graph?

A   The highest frequency of cases within the population was in the 70–74 year old age group.

B   As the age group increases, the frequency of cases within the population always increases.

C   When there were 4800 new cases, the frequency of cases within the population was 600 per 100 000.

D   The greatest increase in the number of new cases, between consecutive age groups, occurred between 55–59 and 60–64.

Page two

3. The graph shows how the concentration of product changes during an enzyme-controlled reaction.

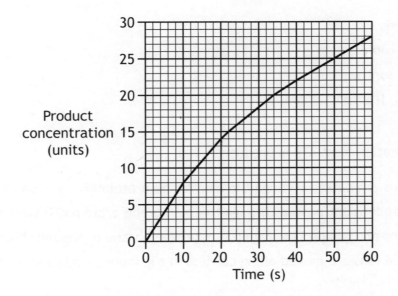

How long does it take the product concentration to reach 50% of its final concentration?

A   20 s

B   22 s

C   25 s

D   28 s

4. A metabolic pathway is shown.

| metabolite P | *enzyme 1* → | metabolite Q | *enzyme 2* → | metabolite R | *enzyme 3* → | metabolite S |

In end-product inhibition

A   enzyme 3 binds to enzyme 1

B   enzyme 3 binds to metabolite P

C   metabolite S binds to enzyme 1

D   metabolite S binds to metabolite P.

[Turn over

5. Mature red blood cells have no nucleus and no mitochondria.

   Which of the following processes can be carried out by a mature red blood cell?

   A   Glycolysis

   B   Cell division

   C   Protein synthesis

   D   Electron transport chain

6. During respiration most ATP is produced when

   A   electrons are passed through the membrane protein ATP synthase

   B   hydrogen ions are passed through the membrane protein ATP synthase

   C   electrons are pumped through the outer membrane of the mitochondrion

   D   hydrogen ions are moved along carriers in the inner membrane of the mitochondrion.

7. Which of the following equations summarises the conversion of glucose to lactic acid?

   A   glucose ⟶ pyruvate ⟶ lactic acid
       ADP + Pi   ATP   NAD   NADH

   B   glucose ⟶ pyruvate ⟶ lactic acid
       ATP   ADP + Pi   NAD   NADH

   C   glucose ⟶ pyruvate ⟶ lactic acid
       ADP + Pi   ATP   NADH   NAD

   D   glucose ⟶ pyruvate ⟶ lactic acid
       ATP   ADP + Pi   NADH   NAD

8. The diagram shows the inheritance of familial hypercholesterolaemia (FH) in three generations of a family.

FH is caused by an autosomal dominant allele.

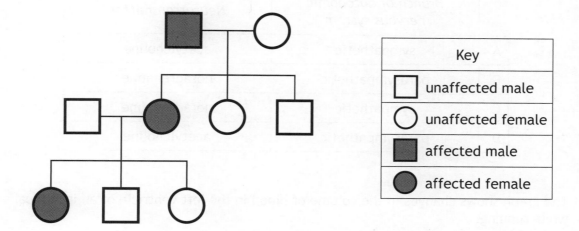

How many individuals in this family are homozygous dominant for this condition?

A   0

B   1

C   2

D   3

9. Red-green colour vision deficiency is a sex-linked recessive condition.

Females heterozygous for the condition are described as being 'carriers'.

A colour vision deficient woman and an unaffected man have children.

Which of the following show the expected phenotypic ratio of the children?

A   1 carrier   :   1 colour vision
     daughter   deficient son

B   1 unaffected   :   1 colour vision
     daughter   deficient son

C   1 unaffected   :   1 colour vision   :   1 unaffected   :   1 carrier
     daughter   deficient son   son   daughter

D   1 carrier   :   1 colour vision   :   1 unaffected   :   1 colour vision
     daughter   deficient son   son   deficient daughter

[Turn over

Page five

10. Which row in the table shows how the autonomic nervous system controls an increase in heart rate?

	Branch of autonomic nervous system	Neurotransmitter
A	sympathetic	acetylcholine
B	parasympathetic	noradrenaline
C	sympathetic	noradrenaline
D	parasympathetic	acetylcholine

11. The graph shows changes in the volume of blood in the left ventricle of an individual's heart while running.

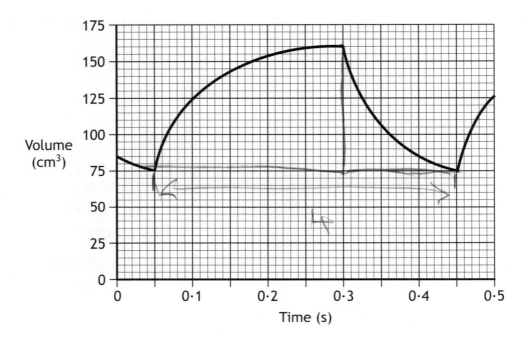

The cardiac output of this individual is

A   5 100 cm³/min

B   10 200 cm³/min

C   12 750 cm³/min

D   24 000 cm³/min.

12. During clot formation, thrombin

A   forms prothrombin

B   causes formation of fibrin threads

C   causes the release of clotting factors

D   forms a meshwork that clots the blood.

13. The flow diagram shows how the concentration of glucose in the blood is controlled during exercise.

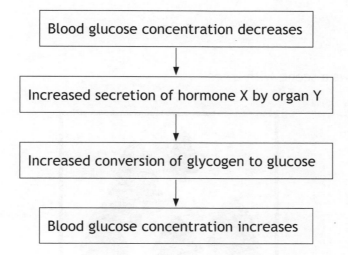

Which row in the table identifies hormone X and organ Y?

	Hormone X	Organ Y
A	insulin	liver
B	glucagon	liver
C	insulin	pancreas
D	glucagon	pancreas

14. A person is 170 cm tall and weighs 70 kg.

They have a body mass index (BMI) of

A   2·4

B   24·2

C   28·8

D   41·2.

[Turn over

15. The following list shows three areas of the brain.

    1   Cortex

    2   Limbic system

    3   Corpus callosum

    Which of these areas are involved in storing spatial memories?

    A   1 only

    B   2 only

    C   1 and 2 only

    D   1, 2 and 3

16. The picture shows a scene with trees.

    What visual cues are used in the perception of depth in this picture?

    1   Relative size

    2   Relative height

    3   Superimposition

    4   Perceptual constancy

    A   1 only

    B   1 and 2 only

    C   1, 2 and 3 only

    D   1, 2, 3 and 4

17. Some individuals who suffer head injuries forget the events that happened a few seconds before the injury occurred.

This memory loss is most likely to be due to the injury affecting

A   retrieval

B   displacement

C   long-term memory

D   short-term memory.

18. Three groups of students were asked to make paper aeroplanes.

Each student had to make five aeroplanes.

The table shows the conditions under which each group worked.

Group	Written set of instructions supplied	Demonstration given on how to fold the paper	Prize awarded to the first student finished
1	yes	no	no
2	no	yes	no
3	no	no	yes

What behavioural term is used to describe the method of learning used by group 2 only?

A   Shaping

B   Imitation

C   Trial and error

D   Reinforcement

[Turn over for next question

19. The table shows the numbers of different types of white blood cells found in blood samples taken from a healthy person and from three different patients.

Type of white blood cell	White blood cells found in blood sample (cells/mm^3)			
	Healthy person	Patient X	Patient Y	Patient Z
Phagocyte	7000	7000	8000	7000
Lymphocyte	3000	2000	3000	3500
Mast cell	1000	1000	1000	1500

Use the information above to match each condition to the correct patient.

	Condition		
	Allergic response	HIV	Infected wound
A	Y	X	Z
B	X	Z	Y
C	Z	Y	X
D	Z	X	Y

20. Which term would be used to describe a global outbreak of an infectious disease?

A   Endemic

B   Sporadic

C   Epidemic

D   Pandemic

[END OF SECTION 1. NOW ATTEMPT THE QUESTIONS IN SECTION 2 OF YOUR QUESTION AND ANSWER BOOKLET.]

National Qualifications 2017

Mark

X740/76/01

Human Biology Section 1 — Answer Grid and Section 2

TUESDAY, 23 MAY
1:00 PM — 3:30 PM

Fill in these boxes and read what is printed below.

Full name of centre

Town

Forename(s)

Surname

Number of seat

Date of birth

Day	Month	Year	Scottish candidate number

Total marks — 100

SECTION 1 — 20 marks

Attempt ALL questions.

Instructions for the completion of Section 1 are given on *Page two*.

SECTION 2 — 80 marks

Attempt ALL questions.

Question 12 contains a choice.

Write your answers clearly in the spaces provided in this booklet. Additional space for answers and rough work is provided at the end of this booklet. If you use this space you must clearly identify the question number you are attempting. Any rough work must be written in this booklet. You should score through your rough work when you have written your final copy.

Use **blue** or **black** ink.

Before leaving the examination room you must give this booklet to the Invigilator; if you do not, you may lose all the marks for this paper.

SECTION 1 — 20 marks

The questions for Section 1 are contained in the question paper X740/76/02.

Read these and record your answers on the answer grid on *Page three* opposite.

Use **blue** or **black** ink. Do NOT use gel pens or pencil.

1.   The answer to each question is **either** A, B, C or D. Decide what your answer is, then fill in the appropriate bubble (see sample question below).

2.   There is **only one correct** answer to each question.

3.   Any rough working should be done on the additional space for answers and rough work at the end of this booklet.

Sample Question

The digestive enzyme pepsin is most active in the

    A   mouth

    B   stomach

    C   duodenum

    D   pancreas.

The correct answer is **B** — stomach. The answer **B** bubble has been clearly filled in (see below).

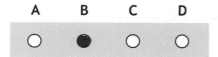

Changing an answer

If you decide to change your answer, cancel your first answer by putting a cross through it (see below) and fill in the answer you want. The answer below has been changed to **D**.

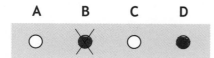

If you then decide to change back to an answer you have already scored out, put a tick (✓) to the **right** of the answer you want, as shown below:

SECTION 1 — Answer Grid

	A	B	C	D
1	○	○	○	○
2	○	○	○	○
3	○	○	○	○
4	○	○	○	○
5	○	○	○	○
6	○	○	○	○
7	○	○	○	○
8	○	○	○	○
9	○	○	○	○
10	○	○	○	○
11	○	○	○	○
12	○	○	○	○
13	○	○	○	○
14	○	○	○	○
15	○	○	○	○
16	○	○	○	○
17	○	○	○	○
18	○	○	○	○
19	○	○	○	○
20	○	○	○	○

[BLANK PAGE]

DO NOT WRITE ON THIS PAGE

[Turn over for next question

DO NOT WRITE ON THIS PAGE

MARKS | DO NOT WRITE IN THIS MARGIN

SECTION 2 — 80 marks

Attempt ALL questions

Question 12 contains a choice

1.   The diagram shows some stages in the development of blood cells.

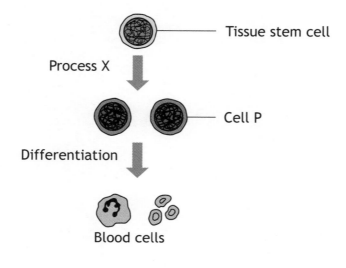

Tissue stem cell

Process X

Cell P

Differentiation

Blood cells

(a)   Name process X.   **1**

_____

(b)   Name the tissue type to which blood cells belong.   **1**

_____

(c)   Explain why red blood cells contain haemoglobin after differentiation but white blood cells do not.   **1**

_____

_____

_____

(d)   Describe how a tumour might develop from cell P.   **1**

_____

_____

_____

MARKS | DO NOT WRITE IN THIS MARGIN

1. **(continued)**

(e) Cancer patients can be treated using chemotherapy.

This treatment destroys tumour cells but also reduces the number of white blood cells. As a result, patients have a higher chance of infection.

The graph shows the white blood cell count of a cancer patient and their chance of infection in the days following chemotherapy treatment.

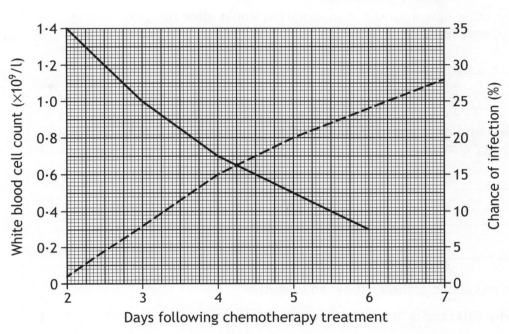

Key

——————— White blood cell count

– – – – – – Chance of infection

(i) State the chance of infection after treatment when the white blood cell count was $0.7 \times 10^9/l$.

1

_____ %

(ii) Predict the white blood cell count seven days following chemotherapy treatment.

1

_____ $\times 10^9/l$

[Turn over

MARKS | DO NOT WRITE IN THIS MARGIN

2. Phenylketonuria (PKU) is an example of a genetic disorder which affects the following metabolic pathway.

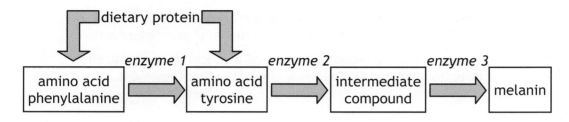

(a) In PKU enzyme 1 is faulty.

(i) Describe how a substitution mutation would alter the gene coding for enzyme 1.   **1**

(ii) Explain how a substitution mutation may cause the synthesis of a faulty enzyme.   **1**

(b) Use the metabolic pathway above to suggest

(i) why PKU results in a build-up of phenylalanine;   **1**

(ii) why individuals with PKU can still produce melanin.   **1**

MARKS | DO NOT WRITE IN THIS MARGIN

2. **(continued)**

(c) Babies born with PKU can develop brain damage from the build-up of phenylalanine and its harmful metabolites.

(i) All babies are tested for PKU immediately after birth.

State the term used to describe this type of diagnostic testing.   1

_____

(ii) Describe how brain damage can be prevented in babies diagnosed with PKU.   1

_____

_____

(d) PKU is caused by an autosomal recessive allele.

A couple, who are both unaffected, have a child who has PKU.

Calculate the percentage chance of their next child having this disorder.   1

Space for calculation

_____ %

[Turn over

3. An investigation was carried out into the effect of a competitive inhibitor on the activity of phosphatase at different substrate concentrations.

   Phosphatase is an enzyme which catalyses the reaction shown.

$$\text{phenolphthalein phosphate} \xrightarrow{\text{phosphatase}} \text{phenolphthalein} + \text{phosphate}$$

   Substrate   **Products**

   Six test tubes each containing a different concentration of substrate were set up. The inhibitor and then the enzyme were added to each tube.

   Figure 1 shows the contents of each tube.

   After 30 minutes, 1 cm^3 of alkali was added to each tube.

   Phenolphthalein turns pink in the presence of alkali. The more phenolphthalein produced, the more intense the pink colour and the higher the absorbance reading measured by a colorimeter.

   Table 1 shows the results of the investigation.

Figure 1

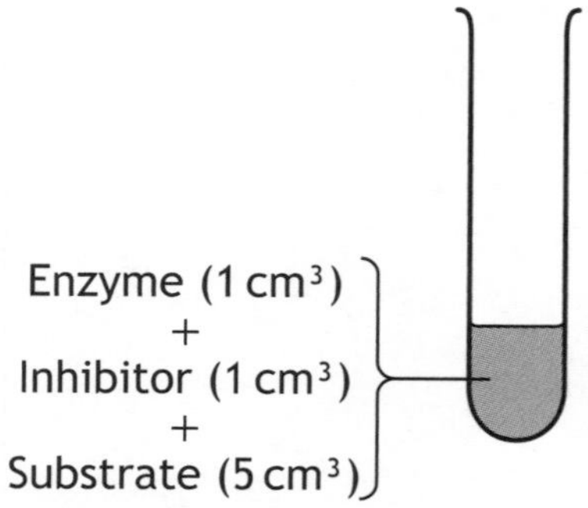

Enzyme (1 cm^3)
+
Inhibitor (1 cm^3)
+
Substrate (5 cm^3)

Table 1

Concentration of substrate (M)	Absorbance (units)
0·05	0·20
0·10	0·30
0·20	0·48
0·40	0·64
0·60	0·78
0·80	0·90

(a) Suggest why alkali was **not** added to each tube at the start of the investigation.

1

_____

_____

(b) State **two** variables, other than those shown above, which should be kept constant to make this investigation valid.

2

1 _____

2 _____

3.   (continued)

MARKS

(c)   Construct a line graph to show the data in **Table 1**.   2

(Additional graph paper, if required, can be found on *Page twenty-eight*.)

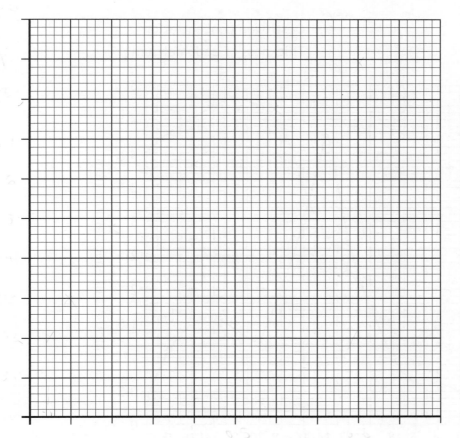

(d)   It was concluded that increasing substrate concentration reduces the effect of the competitive inhibitor.

Explain how the results of this investigation support this conclusion.   2

_____

_____

_____

_____

(e)   Suggest how the results of this investigation would be different if a non-competitive inhibitor had been used.   1

_____

_____

MARKS DO NOT WRITE IN THIS MARGIN

4. The graph shows how the plasma concentration of oestrogen and the thickness of the endometrium vary during a woman's menstrual cycle.

Key
—o— Oestrogen concentration
--x-- Thickness of endometrium

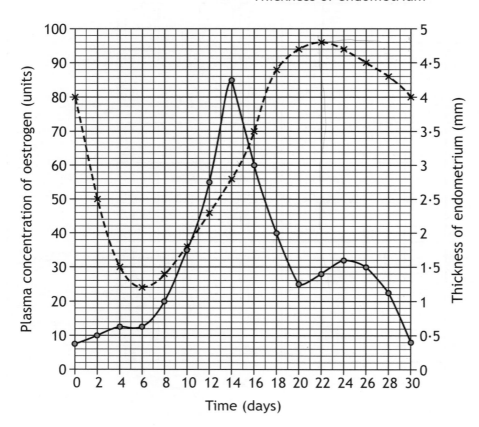

(a) Ovulation occurs on day 15 of this cycle.

(i) Describe the role of oestrogen in triggering this event.   1

_____

_____

_____

(ii) State the thickness of the endometrium on day 15.   1

_____ mm

MARKS | DO NOT WRITE IN THIS MARGIN

4. **(continued)**

(b) (i) Express, as a simple whole number ratio, the thickness of the endometrium on day 6 compared to day 22.   **1**

Space for calculation

_____ : _____
Day 6   Day 22

(ii) Oestrogen stimulates thickening of the endometrium.

Describe evidence from the graph which indicates that another factor also stimulates thickening of the endometrium.   **1**

_____

_____

_____

(c) Suggest **one** way in which the graph for the next menstrual cycle would differ from this one if the woman became pregnant during that cycle.   **1**

_____

_____

(d) State how fertility drugs stimulate ovulation.   **1**

_____

_____

[Turn over

MARKS | DO NOT WRITE IN THIS MARGIN

5. The diagram represents a capillary network, associated vessels and cells.

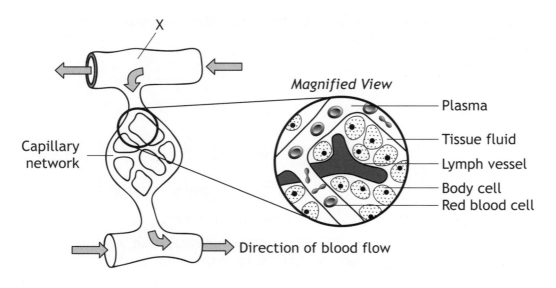

(a) (i) Name the type of blood vessel labelled X.   1

_____

(ii) State how blood vessel X can reduce blood flow to the capillary network.   1

_____

_____

(b) (i) Name the layer of cells which forms the wall of a capillary.   1

_____

(ii) Describe how substances pass from plasma to tissue fluid.   1

_____

_____

(iii) Name a type of molecule which is present in plasma but absent in tissue fluid.   1

_____

(c) Describe **one** role of the lymph vessel in the diagram.   1

_____

_____

MARKS | DO NOT WRITE IN THIS MARGIN

6. The picture shows a man having his blood pressure measured.

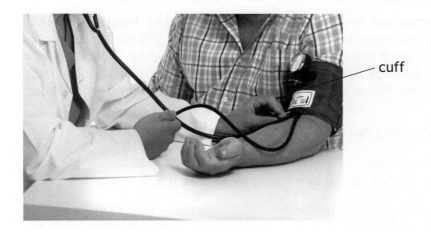

cuff

(a) A blood pressure reading consists of a high systolic value and a lower diastolic value.

Explain the difference between these two values.

1

_____

_____

_____

(b) Suggest a reason why the pulse in the man's left wrist stops when the cuff is inflated.

1

_____

_____

(c) The man's blood pressure was measured as 160/100.

(i) Explain how atherosclerosis could have caused this high blood pressure.

2

_____

_____

_____

_____

(ii) The man's blood HDL to LDL ratio was lower than normal.

Describe how this may have contributed to atherosclerosis.

1

_____

_____

[Turn over

7. Hormone replacement therapy (HRT) is used by women to relieve symptoms of the menopause, which usually occurs from around the age of 50.

A study was carried out into the effects of HRT on the health of 12 000 women. The women were separated into three equal groups according to their age. Half of each group took a daily HRT tablet while the other half received a placebo. Over the next five years the number of women in each group who developed either a pulmonary embolism or coronary heart disease was recorded.

The results are shown in the table.

| | Conditions developed by women in the study | | | |
| | Pulmonary Embolism | | Coronary Heart Disease | |
Age group (years)	Number of cases in women given HRT	Number of cases in women given a placebo	Number of cases in women given HRT	Number of cases in women given a placebo
50—59	10	5	20	18
60—69	20	12	35	33
70—79	30	15	80	76

(a) Describe **two** trends shown by the results for pulmonary embolism. 2

1 _____

_____

2 _____

_____

(b) It was concluded that taking HRT has no effect on the risk of coronary heart disease.

Explain why the results of the study support this conclusion. 1

_____

_____

(c) Suggest a factor, other than HRT, which could have influenced the results of this study. 1

_____

MARKS | DO NOT WRITE IN THIS MARGIN

7.   (continued)

(d)   Describe how the researchers attempted to make sure that the results of this study were reliable.

1

_____

_____

(e)   HRT can be prescribed to treat osteoporosis, a condition which increases the risk of bones thinning and breaking.

The graph shows how the average bone mass of women changes with age.

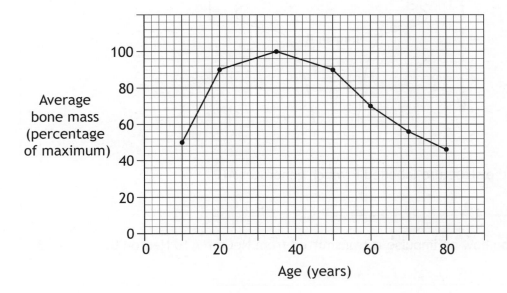

(i)   **Use data from the graph** to describe the changes that occur in the average bone mass between the ages of 10 and 80.

2

_____

_____

_____

_____

(ii)   State the number of years the average bone mass of women is at least 80% of the maximum.

1

_____ years

[Turn over

MARKS | DO NOT WRITE IN THIS MARGIN

8. The diagram represents two neurons and the synapse between them.

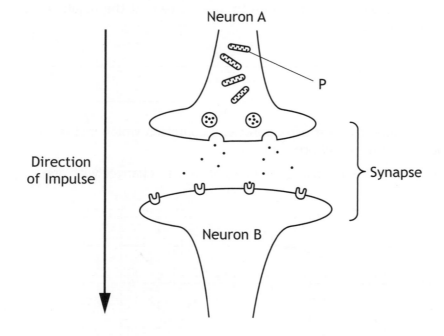

Neuron A

P

Direction of Impulse

Synapse

Neuron B

(a) Name the structure labelled P which generates ATP.

1

_____

(b) Describe how an impulse is transmitted from Neuron A to Neuron B.

3

MARKS | DO NOT WRITE IN THIS MARGIN

8.   (continued)

(c)   Many drugs which affect synapses may cause sensitisation over a period of time.

Describe the effect that sensitisation has on the synapse and the consequences for the individual.

2

Effect_____

_____

Consequences _____

_____

[Turn over

MARKS | DO NOT WRITE IN THIS MARGIN

9. Sympathetic and parasympathetic nerves regulate heart rate.

(a) Name the part of the brain that regulates the heart rate.   1

_____

(b) The sympathetic and parasympathetic nerves work antagonistically. Explain what this statement means.   1

_____

_____

(c) An investigation was carried out to determine the effects these nerves have on heart rate by firstly blocking the sympathetic nerve and then blocking both nerves.

The graph shows the results of the investigation.

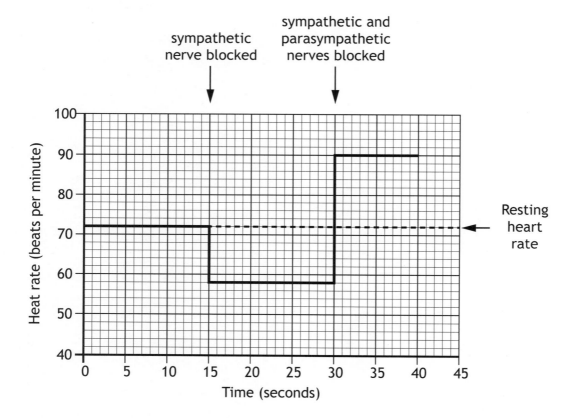

(i) State the heart rate when only the sympathetic nerve is blocked.   1

_____beats per minute

MARKS | DO NOT WRITE IN THIS MARGIN

9. **(c)** **(continued)**

(ii) Calculate the increase in the heart rate which then occurs when the parasympathetic nerve is also blocked.

1

_____beats per minute

(d) Explain why the heart continues to contract when both nerves are blocked.

1

_____

_____

(e) The parasympathetic nerve has a greater effect on the resting heart rate than the sympathetic nerve.

Use information from the graph to justify this statement.

1

_____

_____

_____

(f) State **one** other effect the sympathetic nervous system has on the body.

1

_____

_____

[Turn over

MARKS | DO NOT WRITE IN THIS MARGIN

10. The diagram shows some of the stages leading to the production of a clone of T lymphocytes by the immune system in response to infection by a pathogen.

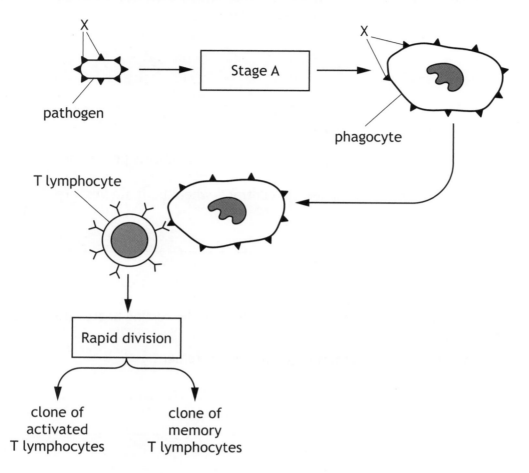

(a) Name the structures labelled X.

1

_____

(b) Describe what happens during Stage A.

2

_____

_____

_____

_____

(c) Name the chemicals which aid the movement of T lymphocytes to the site of infection.

1

_____

MARKS

DO NOT
WRITE IN
THIS
MARGIN

10. **(continued)**

(d) The diagram shows how a clone of memory T lymphocytes is produced.
Describe an advantage of having memory cells.

1

_____

_____

(e) State how a tuberculosis (TB) pathogen avoids immune detection.

1

_____

_____

[Turn over

MARKS | DO NOT WRITE IN THIS MARGIN

11. **Table 1** contains information about the life expectancy of Scottish children between 1861 and 2011.

Life expectancy is the additional number of years a person is expected to survive from a given age.

Table 1

Year	Average life expectancy of child (years)		
	from birth	from age 1	from age 15
1861	42	47	43
1891	46	52	46
1921	55	59	50
1951	66	68	55
1981	72	72	59
2011	78	77	63

(a) (i) Calculate the percentage increase in life expectancy for children born in 2011 compared to children born in 1861.

    Space for calculation

1

_____ %

(ii) Give the 30 year period during which the greatest increase in life expectancy from birth occurred.

1

From _____ to _____

(iii) Suggest **two** reasons for an increase in life expectancy over the 150 year period.

2

1 _____

_____

2 _____

_____

MARKS | DO NOT WRITE IN THIS MARGIN

11.　(continued)

(b)　**Table 2** contains information about the life span of Scottish children.

Life span is the number of years a person lives for.

Table 2

Year	Average Life Span (years)		
	from birth	from age 1	from age 15
1861	42	48	58
2011			

(i)　**Use the information in Table 1 to complete Table 2** to indicate the expected average life span of children in 2011.　　1

(ii)　Suggest why the figures for 1861 increase from 42 to 58 years.　　1

_____

_____

[Turn over

MARKS | DO NOT WRITE IN THIS MARGIN

12. Answer **either** A **or** B in the space below.

Labelled diagrams may be used where appropriate.

A   Describe the structure of DNA and the process of DNA replication.   **9**

OR

B   Describe the structure of RNA and the process of transcription.   **9**

MARKS | DO NOT WRITE IN THIS MARGIN

ADDITIONAL SPACE FOR ANSWER to Question 12

[END OF QUESTION PAPER]

ADDITIONAL SPACE FOR ANSWERS AND ROUGH WORK

Additional graph paper for Question 3 (c)

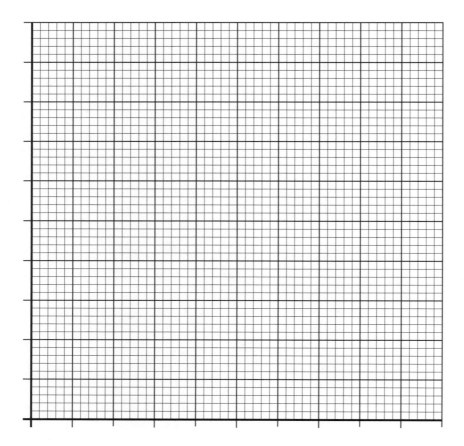

HIGHER

2018

National Qualifications 2018

X740/76/02

Human Biology
Section 1 — Questions

TUESDAY, 15 MAY

1:00 PM – 3:30 PM

Instructions for the completion of Section 1 are given on *Page two* of your question and answer booklet X740/76/01.

Record your answers on the answer grid on *Page three* of your question and answer booklet.

Before leaving the examination room you must give your question and answer booklet to the Invigilator; if you do not, you may lose all the marks for this paper.

SECTION 1 — 20 marks

Attempt ALL questions

1. Each type of human cell has a different structure and function because

    A   they contain different genes
    B   different genes are expressed in each
    C   some genes are lost during differentiation
    D   some genes are gained during differentiation.

2. Which pathway describes the production of haploid gametes from diploid germline cells?

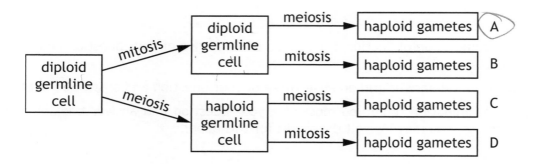

3. The table shows the number of dividing and non-dividing cells in samples of three types of tissue.

Type of tissue	Number of cells dividing	Number of cells not dividing
nerve	8	17
blood	4	16
muscle	1	19

The percentage of connective tissue cells which are dividing is

    A   5%
    B   20%
    C   25%
    D   32%

4. A fragment of DNA contained 144 nucleotide base pairs.

What is the total number of deoxyribose sugars in this fragment?

A   48

B   72

C   144

D   288

5. The table shows the positions of bases in the mRNA codons for specific amino acids.

First position	Second position				Third position
	U	C	A	G	
U	phenylalanine	serine	tyrosine	cysteine	U
					C
	leucine		stop	stop	A
			stop	tryptophan	G
C	leucine	proline	histidine	arginine	U
					C
			glutamine		A
					G
A	isoleucine	threonine	asparagine	serine	U
					C
	start/ methionine		lysine	arginine	A
					G
G	valine	alanine	aspartic acid	glycine	U
					C
			glutamic acid		A
					G

Which of the following mutations in a section of mRNA would result in the production of a shortened protein?

	Original mRNA codons	Mutated mRNA codons
A	..... AUG GCC CAU	..... AUG GCA CAU .....
B	..... CAG UAC GUG	..... CAG UAG GUG .....
C	..... AAU UGG CCA	..... AAU UGU CCA .....
D	..... GUC AAC UCG	..... GUC AAG UCG .....

6. A mature mRNA transcript is produced from a primary mRNA transcript by

    A   adding exons

    B   adding introns

    C   removing exons

    D   removing introns.

7. DNA probes are short fragments of DNA that

    A   allow RNA polymerase to begin transcription

    B   allow DNA polymerase to begin DNA replication

    C   are used to detect specific sequences in samples of DNA

    D   bind to specific target sequences in the PCR reaction to amplify DNA.

8. The list shows some of the substances produced during the respiration of glucose in the presence of oxygen.

    1   acetyl group

    2   pyruvate

    3   citrate

    4   ATP

    Which of the following sequences shows the order in which these substances are produced?

    A   4, 2, 1, 3

    B   4, 2, 3, 1

    C   2, 1, 4, 3

    D   2, 3, 1, 4

9. In cellular respiration, the products of the electron transport chain are

    A   water and ATP

    B   oxygen and ATP

    C   NADH and $FADH_2$

    D   carbon dioxide and water.

10. The following diagram shows an enzyme-controlled metabolic pathway.

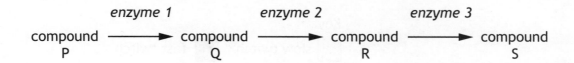

If enzyme 2 is inhibited at time X, which graph predicts the resulting concentrations of compounds Q and R?

A

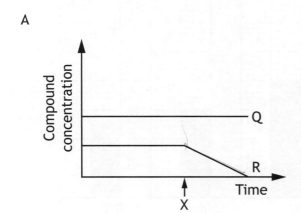

B

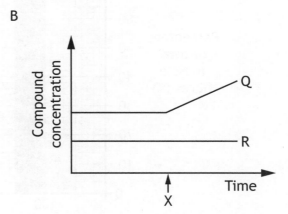

C

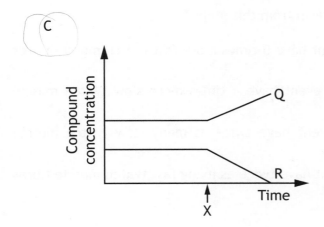

D

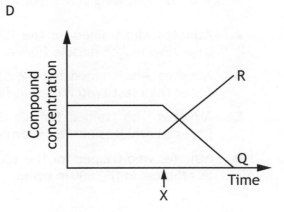

[Turn over

11. The graph shows the percentage of slow and fast twitch muscle fibres present in athletes who trained for events of different distances.

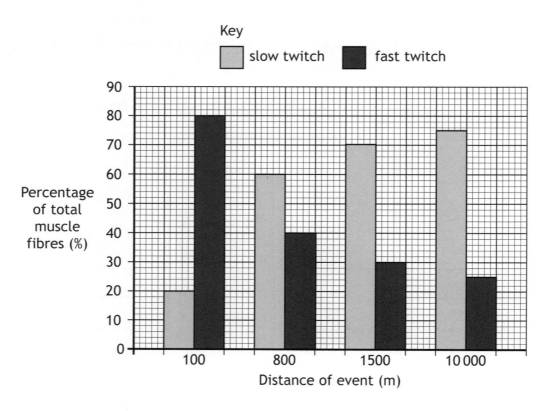

Which of the following conclusions can be drawn from this graph?

A   Athletes who trained for the 100 m event have 5 times more fast twitch muscle fibres than slow twitch muscle fibres.

B   Athletes who trained for the 10 000 m event have 4 times more slow twitch muscle fibres than fast twitch muscle fibres.

C   Athletes who trained for the 800 m event have twice as many slow twitch muscle fibres as athletes in the 1500 m event.

D   Athletes who trained for the 100 m event have twice as many fast twitch muscle fibres as athletes in the 800 m event.

12. The mitochondria of human cells contain DNA.

Women can pass mitochondrial DNA to their offspring but men cannot.

The diagram shows a family tree.

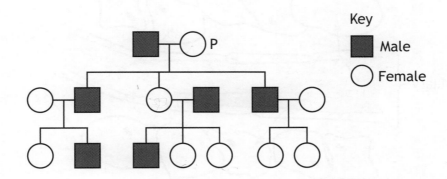

Identify the number of individuals in the family tree that have inherited mitochondrial DNA which originated from P.

A   3

B   4

C   5

D   6

13. Thalassaemia is an inherited condition that affects the ability of haemoglobin to carry oxygen. The condition is **not** sex-linked.

The table shows genotypes and phenotypes associated with thalassaemia.

Genotype	Phenotype
AA	unaffected
AT	thalassaemia trait
TT	severe thalassaemia

An unaffected man and a woman with thalassaemia trait have a child.

The chance that the child will also have thalassaemia trait is

A   0%

B   25%

C   50%

D   100%

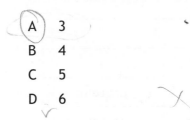

[Turn over

14. The diagram shows the movement of substances between a capillary and the surrounding liver tissue cells.

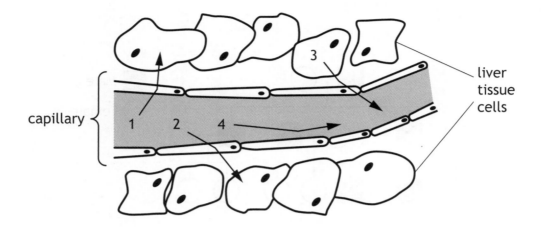

Which row in the table identifies the substances in the diagram?

	Substance			
	1	2	3	4
A	glucose	carbon dioxide	oxygen	protein
B	oxygen	glucose	carbon dioxide	protein
C	protein	glucose	oxygen	carbon dioxide
D	protein	oxygen	carbon dioxide	glucose

15. During the formation of a thrombus, fibrin

A converts prothrombin to thrombin

B causes the formation of fibrinogen

C forms a meshwork to clot the blood

D causes the release of clotting factors.

16.   The diagrams show two ways to classify the nervous system.

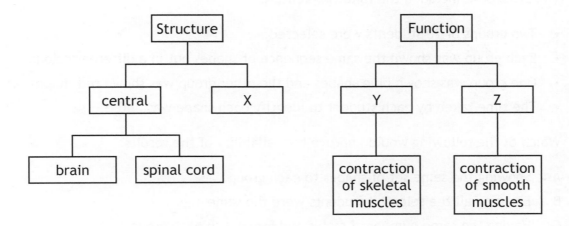

Which row in the table identifies X, Y and Z?

	Nervous System		
	X	Y	Z
A	peripheral	somatic	autonomic
B	somatic	autonomic	peripheral
C	autonomic	peripheral	somatic
D	peripheral	autonomic	somatic

17.   A child was stung by a wasp. This led to them being afraid of all flying insects.
       This is an example of

A   discrimination

B   generalisation

C   internalisation

D   reinforcement.

[Turn over

18. An investigation was carried out into the effect of colour on the recognition of shapes. The procedure included the following features.

- Two groups of 20 students were selected.
- Each group was shown the same sequence of shapes but in a different colour.
- One group was shown blue shapes and the other group was shown red shapes.
- The time taken by each student to identify each shape was noted.

Which of the following would improve the reliability of the results?

A Showing the same set of shapes to each group.

B Ensuring all the selected students were the same age.

C Having the same number of males and females in each group.

D Repeating the whole procedure with two more groups of students.

19. The virus that causes influenza can evade the specific immune response by

A attacking phagocytes

B attacking lymphocytes

C surviving within phagocytes

D showing antigenic variation.

20. A hospital introduced a programme of handwashing in 2008.

The graph shows the impact of this on the number of cases of two infections.

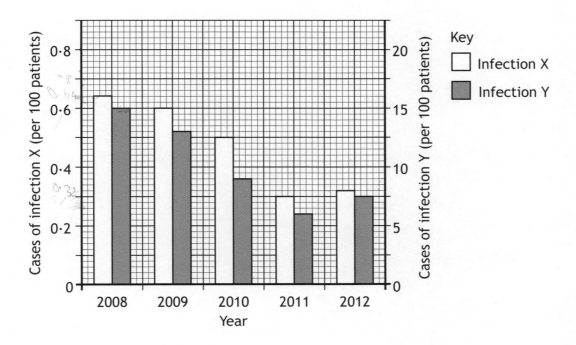

Which of the following statements is **not** correct?

A The cases of both infections fell by 50% over the 5 year period.

B The number of cases of infection Y was always greater than the number of cases of infection X.

C The highest number of cases of infection X was 0·62 per 100 patients while the highest number of cases of infection Y was 15 per 100 patients.

D The lowest number of cases of infection X was 0·3 per 100 patients while the lowest number of cases of infection Y was 6 per 100 patients.

[END OF SECTION 1. NOW ATTEMPT THE QUESTIONS IN SECTION 2
OF YOUR QUESTION AND ANSWER BOOKLET.]

[BLANK PAGE]

DO NOT WRITE ON THIS PAGE

Mark

National Qualifications 2018

X740/76/01

**Human Biology
Section 1 — Answer Grid
and Section 2**

TUESDAY, 15 MAY

1:00 PM – 3:30 PM

Fill in these boxes and read what is printed below.

Full name of centre

Town

Forename(s)

Surname

Number of seat

Date of birth

Day	Month	Year	Scottish candidate number

Total marks — 100

SECTION 1 — 20 marks

Attempt ALL questions.

Instructions for the completion of Section 1 are given on *Page two*.

SECTION 2 — 80 marks

Attempt ALL questions.

Question 13 contains a choice.

Write your answers clearly in the spaces provided in this booklet. Additional space for answers and rough work is provided at the end of this booklet. If you use this space you must clearly identify the question number you are attempting. Any rough work must be written in this booklet. You should score through your rough work when you have written your final copy.

Use **blue** or **black** ink.

Before leaving the examination room you must give this booklet to the Invigilator; if you do not, you may lose all the marks for this paper.

SECTION 1 — 20 marks

The questions for Section 1 are contained in the question paper X740/76/02.

Read these and record your answers on the answer grid on *Page three* opposite.

Use **blue** or **black** ink. Do NOT use gel pens or pencil.

1. The answer to each question is **either** A, B, C or D. Decide what your answer is, then fill in the appropriate bubble (see sample question below).

2. There is **only one correct** answer to each question.

3. Any rough working should be done on the additional space for answers and rough work at the end of this booklet.

Sample Question

The digestive enzyme pepsin is most active in the

    A   mouth

    B   stomach

    C   duodenum

    D   pancreas.

The correct answer is **B** — stomach. The answer **B** bubble has been clearly filled in (see below).

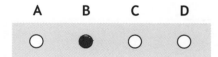

Changing an answer

If you decide to change your answer, cancel your first answer by putting a cross through it (see below) and fill in the answer you want. The answer below has been changed to **D**.

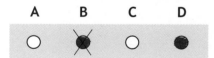

If you then decide to change back to an answer you have already scored out, put a tick (✓) to the **right** of the answer you want, as shown below:

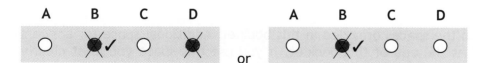

    or

SECTION 1 — Answer Grid

	A	B	C	D
1	○	○	○	○
2	○	○	○	○
3	○	○	○	○
4	○	○	○	○
5	○	○	○	○
6	○	○	○	○
7	○	○	○	○
8	○	○	○	○
9	○	○	○	○
10	○	○	○	○
11	○	○	○	○
12	○	○	○	○
13	○	○	○	○
14	○	○	○	○
15	○	○	○	○
16	○	○	○	○
17	○	○	○	○
18	○	○	○	○
19	○	○	○	○
20	○	○	○	○

[BLANK PAGE]

DO NOT WRITE ON THIS PAGE

MARKS | DO NOT WRITE IN THIS MARGIN

SECTION 2 — 80 marks
Attempt ALL questions
Question 13 contains a choice

1. The diagram represents glycolysis and the metabolic pathway which synthesises lactic acid.

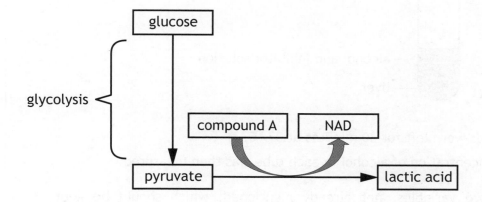

(a) (i) State where glycolysis occurs within a cell.   1

_____

(ii) Describe what happens during the energy investment phase of glycolysis.   1

_____

_____

(b) During lactic acid synthesis NAD is regenerated.

(i) Name compound A.   1

_____

(ii) Explain the importance of the regeneration of NAD for glycolysis.   1

_____

_____

(iii) State the reason why muscle cells produce lactic acid during vigorous exercise.   1

_____

_____

[Turn over

MARKS | DO NOT WRITE IN THIS MARGIN

2. An investigation was carried out into the effect of inhibitor concentration on the activity of an enzyme which breaks down alcohol in liver cells.

Six test tubes were set up, each containing a piece of liver, alcohol and a different concentration of inhibitor, as shown in the diagram.

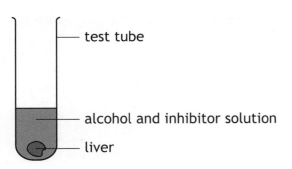

— test tube

— alcohol and inhibitor solution

— liver

The test tubes were left for 30 minutes at 37 °C.

The final concentration of alcohol in each tube was then measured.

(a) State **two** variables, not already mentioned, which should be kept constant to make this investigation valid.

2

1 ___mass of liver___ ✓

2 ___volume of alcohol___ ✓

(b) The inhibitor used in this investigation was non-competitive.

Describe how a non-competitive inhibitor works.

1

___bind to enzyme not on the active site and___

___change the shape of the active site___ ✓

(c) The results of the investigation are shown in the table.

Inhibitor concentration (mM)	Final alcohol concentration (% of initial concentration)
0·5	20
1·5	28
2·5	60
3·5	96
4·5	100
5·5	100

MARKS | DO NOT WRITE IN THIS MARGIN

2. (c) (continued)

(i) Construct a line graph to show the data in the table.

(Additional graph paper, if required, can be found on *Page twenty-seven.*)

2

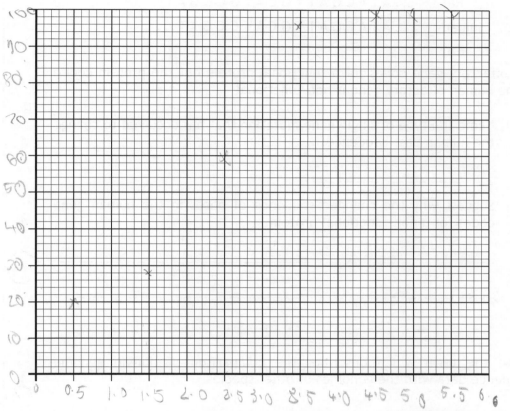

(ii) **Use the data** to describe the relationship between the concentration of inhibitor and enzyme activity.

2

As the inhibitor concentration increased, the final alcohol concentration also increased until a maximum of 100% enzyme activity (100) ✗

(d) A second experiment, using increasing concentrations of alcohol, was carried out to show that the inhibitor was non-competitive.

Six test tubes were set up, each containing a piece of liver, an inhibitor concentration of 4·5 mM and different concentrations of alcohol.

Suggest how the results would confirm that the inhibitor was non-competitive.

1

because increasing substrate concentration does not overcome non-competitive inhibition

[**Turn over**

MARKS | DO NOT WRITE IN THIS MARGIN

3. Olfactory genes code for receptors in the nose that detect smells.

    The base sequences from the same region of a rat olfactory gene and a human olfactory gene are shown.

    Rat   ...A T A C G A T T G C A T G C C G A T...
    Human   ...A T A C G A T T G C A T C C G A T...

    The rat olfactory gene codes for a functional protein but the protein coded for by the human olfactory gene is non-functional.

    (a) (i) Name the type of single gene mutation that has occurred to change the human base sequence.   1

        deletion ✓

        (ii) Suggest why the changed sequence of bases in the human gene codes for a non-functional protein.   1

        because the codon will produce a
        different amino acid ?
        ↳ order / sequence of amino acids would
        change

    (b) State the term which describes the comparison of human genome sequence data with the genomes of other species.   1

        bioinformatics?   +
        systematics

MARKS | DO NOT WRITE IN THIS MARGIN

3. (continued)

(c) The table shows the number of functional olfactory genes identified in rats, humans and chickens.

Animal	Number of functional olfactory genes
rat	1200
human	400
chicken	80

(i) Express, as a simple whole number ratio, the number of functional olfactory genes found in the animals.

1

Space for calculation

1200   400   80
120   40   8
30   10   2
,5   :   5   :   1
rat   human   chicken

(ii) Suggest what the number of functional olfactory genes indicates about the sense of smell of these animals.

1

The more olfactory genes there is, the better the sense of smell.

(d) Describe **two** chromosome structure mutations and the overall consequence of these to the individual.

3

inversion - is where a section of chromosome is switched around. This won't have a huge impact on the protein because only 1 amino acid is changed   ✗

Translocation - is when a section of chromosome is added but not to its homologous partner. This will have a huge impact on the protein because all amino acids after the mutation will be affected. ✓

MARKS | DO NOT WRITE IN THIS MARGIN

4. The graph contains information about breastfeeding and infant mortality in a country between 2005 and 2012.

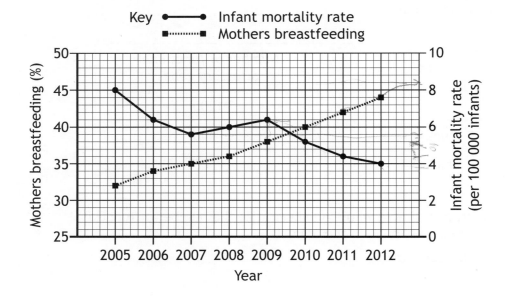

(a)   (i) State the infant mortality rate when 35% of mothers were breastfeeding.   **1**

_____5·6_____   ✓ per 100 000

(ii) Calculate the percentage decrease in the infant mortality rate between 2009 and 2012.   **1**

Space for calculation

$= \dfrac{2·4}{6·4} \times 100 =$

6·4 − 4

_____37·5_____ %

(iii) Predict the percentage of mothers who would be breastfeeding in 2013.   **1**

_____46_____ %

(iv) Describe evidence from the graph which indicates that the increase in breastfeeding mothers cannot be the only reason for the decrease in infant mortality.   **1**

because it increased between 2007 to
2009 even though there was an increase
in mothers breastfeeding ✓

Page ten

MARKS | DO NOT WRITE IN THIS MARGIN

4.   (continued)

(b)   The table contains information from a Scottish survey comparing the incidence of diarrhoea in breastfed and bottle fed babies.

	Age of baby (months)			
	0—3		4—6	
Feeding method	Breast	Bottle	Breast	Bottle
Incidence of diarrhoea (%)	3·6	21·6	10·2	20·4

(i)   Calculate how many times greater the incidence of diarrhoea is when 0—3 month old babies are bottle fed rather than breastfed.   **1**

Space for calculation

$$\frac{21 \cdot 6}{3 \cdot 6} = 6$$

_____ 6 ✓ times greater

(ii)   Diarrhoea is a symptom of an intestinal infection.

Suggest why there is a greater incidence of diarrhoea in bottle fed babies.

because bottle food doesn't have all the same nutrients

/

[Turn over

MARKS | DO NOT WRITE IN THIS MARGIN

5.   The diagram represents part of the autonomic nervous system which links the brain to the heart.

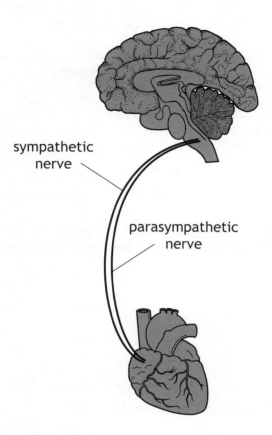

sympathetic nerve

parasympathetic nerve

(a) Name the parts of the brain and heart which are linked by the nerves shown in the diagram.

②

Brain __Medulla__ ✓

Heart ___SAN___ ✓

(b) Explain how the sympathetic and parasympathetic nerves control heart rate.

②

Sympathetic releases noradrenaline, that ✓ increases heart rate ✓

Parasympathetic releases acetylcholine which ✓ decreases heart rate ✓

MARKS | DO NOT WRITE IN THIS MARGIN

5.   (continued)

(c)   The diagram shows an electrocardiogram (ECG) of an individual's heart.

0·2 second

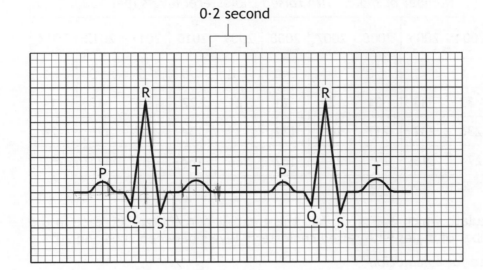

(i)   Use the diagram to calculate the individual's heart rate.   1

Space for calculation

0.8 seconds

$\frac{60}{0.8} = 75$

_____75_____ beats/min

(ii) Describe what happens in the heart between points Q and S.   1

ventricular systole

_____

[Turn over

Page thirteen

6. The table shows the number of males in different age groups with raised cholesterol levels in Scotland between 2004 and 2013.

Age group (years)	Number of males with raised cholesterol levels (per 1000)									
	2004	2005	2006	2007	2008	2009	2010	2011	2012	2013
Under 15	1	1	0	1	0	0	0	2	0	1
15—44	33	33	31	29	21	21	22	16	18	14
45—64	236	232	217	209	132	139	134	137	125	128
Over 64	274	316	295	274	167	166	164	167	171	167

(a) Calculate which age group had the greatest percentage decrease in the number of males with raised cholesterol levels between 2004 and 2013. **1**

Space for calculation

$$\frac{33-14}{33} \times 100 = 57.6\%$$

$$\frac{236-128}{236} \times 100 = 45.8\%$$

$$\frac{274-167}{274} \times 100 = 39\%$$

_____15—44_____ years

(b) (i) Name a type of drug that is used to control cholesterol levels. **1**

____statins____ ✓

(ii) Use the data in the table to identify the year in which this type of drug became widely available. **1**

____2008____ ✓

(c) State **one** role of cholesterol in the body. **1**

to make the sex hormones - progesterone, oestrogen and testosterone ✓

MARKS | DO NOT WRITE IN THIS MARGIN

7. An office worker and an Olympic swimmer were found to have the same BMI. They each weighed 105 kg and were 1·85 m in height.

(a) (i) Calculate their BMI.

        Space for calculation

1

$$\frac{105}{1 \cdot 85^2} = 30 \cdot 7$$

_____ 30·7 ✓ _____

(ii) Suggest why, after calculating their BMI, a health professional advised only the office worker to lose weight.

1

Because a BMI > 30 means that you are overweight.

_____ ✗

(b) The office worker developed Type 2 diabetes.

Explain why this condition causes the blood glucose concentration to remain high.

2

because the receptors in the liver become insensitive to glucose so they require more before their cells will start producing insulin

[Turn over

MARKS | DO NOT WRITE IN THIS MARGIN

8. (a) The diagram represents the flow of information through memory.

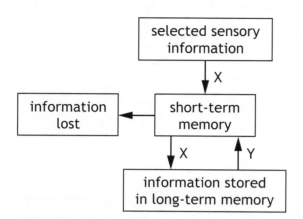

(i) Name process X.

encoding ✓

1

(ii) Explain why information can be lost by displacement from short-term memory.

because it has a maximum capacity of 7 I 2 items ✓

1

(iii) Rehearsal increases the chance of information being transferred from short-term to long-term memory.

Describe **one** other way that information can be transferred from short-term to long-term memory.

elaboration of meaning – giving context behind information and linking it to previous knowledge ✓

1

(iv) Y represents the retrieval of information from long-term memory.

Describe how contextual cues aid the retrieval of information.

because they are the time or place that the memory was encoded ✗ trigger their memory of the

1

(b) State where semantic memories are stored in the brain.

Long term memory ?

1

MARKS | DO NOT WRITE IN THIS MARGIN

9. (a) The photograph shows cars parked in a street.

The judgement of distance depends on visual cues.

Explain how the following visual cues allow a person to judge how far away each car is from them in the street.

(i) Size _____   1

_____

_____

(ii) Superimposition _____   1

_____

_____

(b) State the term used for the ability of the brain to judge the distance of an object based on the different images received by each eye.   1

perspective _____

[Turn over

MARKS | DO NOT WRITE IN THIS MARGIN

9. **(continued)**

(c) Students carried out the following experiment on the judgement of distance.

    1   One student raised their right arm and closed both eyes.

    2   A coin was randomly placed on the bench in front of them.

    3   The student opened both eyes and immediately lowered their arm trying to touch the coin with their index finger.

    4   The distance between the coin and the spot where the index finger landed was measured.

    5   Steps 1—4 were repeated, firstly **only** opening the left eye and secondly **only** opening the right eye.

    6   Then steps 1—5 were repeated another nine times.

The results are shown in the table.

Attempt	Distance between coin and spot where finger landed (mm)		
	both eyes open	left eye open	right eye open
1	2	4	12
2	2	6	15
3	1	6	16
4	1	8	14
5	1	9	13
6	0	5	14
7	0	4	17
8	1	10	18
9	0	7	
10	1	8	15
Average	0·9	6·7	15·0

    (i)   Calculate the missing distance for attempt 9.   1

       Space for calculation

_____ mm

MARKS | DO NOT WRITE IN THIS MARGIN

9. **(c)** **(continued)**

(ii) Suggest a reason why the coin was randomly placed for each attempt. **1**

so they didn't remember where it was placed

(iii) The results of the experiment show that two eyes are more accurate than one for judging distance.

State another conclusion which can be drawn from the results. **1**

left eye was stronger than right

[Turn over

MARKS | DO NOT WRITE IN THIS MARGIN

10. The graph shows the percentage of adult smokers in different age groups in the UK in 2011.

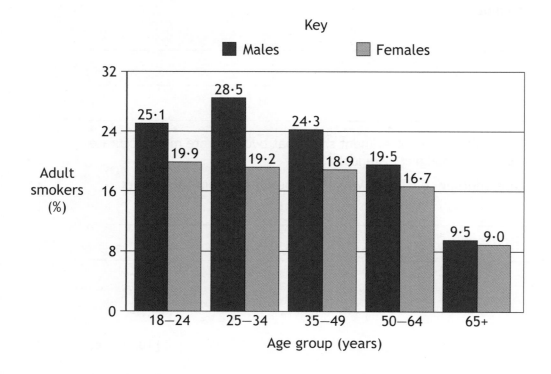

Key

■ Males   ▨ Females

(a) (i) Describe **two** trends shown in the graph.   2

1 _Males are more likely to be smokers_

_____

_____

2 _The number of females smoking_
  is decreasing every year.

_____

(ii) Apart from individuals giving up smoking, suggest a reason for the difference in the percentage of 25—34 year olds and 65+ year olds smoking.   1

_____

_____

MARKS | DO NOT WRITE IN THIS MARGIN

10. (continued)

(b) Smokers can become addicted to the nicotine in tobacco.

Nicotine acts as an agonist of acetylcholine causing an increase in the levels of dopamine.

(i) Describe how nicotine acts as an agonist at a synapse.   1

_____

_____

_____

(ii) Describe how dopamine reinforces smoking behaviour.   1

_____

_____

_____

(iii) Describe how repeated exposure to nicotine can lead to nicotine tolerance by desensitisation.   1

_____

_____

_____

(c) Explain why anti-smoking campaigns often feature a celebrity.   1

_____

_____

_____

(d) In 2011 there were 36 980 cases of lung cancer in the UK linked to smoking. This was 86% of all lung cancer cases in the UK in 2011.

Calculate the total number of lung cancer cases in the UK in 2011.   1

Space for calculation

_____

[Turn over

11. The graph compares the number of cases of a water-borne disease in two countries between 1990 and 1995.

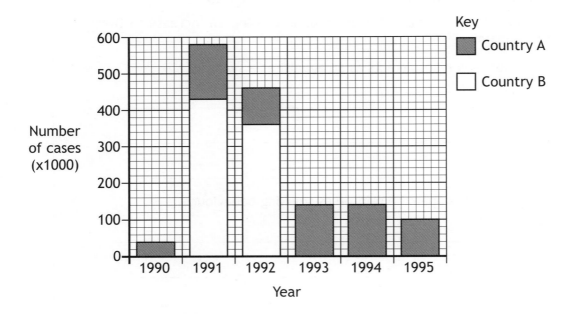

(a) (i) Describe how the graph demonstrates that the pattern of the disease was epidemic in country B.   **1**

_____

_____

_____

(ii) State the term which describes the pattern of disease in country A.   **1**

_____

(iii) Suggest how the pattern of this disease in country A would differ if the disease was sporadic.   **1**

_____

_____

MARKS | DO NOT WRITE IN THIS MARGIN

11. **(continued)**

(b) In 1996, a programme of immunisation against this disease was started in country B. Herd immunity was established once 85% of the population was immunised.

    (i) Explain why this level of immunisation protected the whole population.

1

    (ii) State **one** reason why it is difficult to immunise 100% of a population against a disease.

1

[Turn over

MARKS | DO NOT WRITE IN THIS MARGIN

12. The non-specific immune system provides resistance to infection by physical, chemical and cellular means.

    (a)   (i)   Name the type of cell which forms a physical barrier in the skin.   **1**

            _____

        (ii) In addition to forming a physical barrier, state another way in which these cells resist infection.   **1**

            _____

            _____

    (b) Mast cells initiate the inflammatory response.

        Name the chemical which they release and explain how it increases the supply of fluid into the infected tissue.   **2**

        Chemical _____

        Explanation _____

        _____

    (c)   (i)   The cellular aspect of the non-specific response is provided by two types of white blood cell.

           Complete the table by describing how these cells destroy pathogens.   **2**

Type of cell	How cell destroys pathogens
Phagocyte	
NK cell	

        (ii) State how phagocytes and NK cells stimulate the specific immune response.   **1**

           _____

           _____

MARKS | DO NOT WRITE IN THIS MARGIN

13. Answer **either** A **or** B in the space below.

Labelled diagrams may be used where appropriate.

A   Give an account of hormonal control of puberty and sperm production in males.   **8**

OR

B   Give an account of treatments for male and female infertility.   **8**

ADDITIONAL SPACE FOR ANSWER to Question 13

[END OF QUESTION PAPER]

MARKS | DO NOT WRITE IN THIS MARGIN

ADDITIONAL SPACE FOR ANSWERS AND ROUGH WORK

Additional graph paper for Question 2 (c)(i)

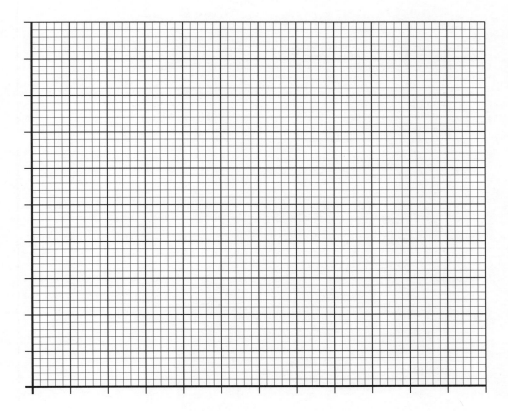

MARKS DO NOT WRITE IN THIS MARGIN

ADDITIONAL SPACE FOR ANSWERS AND ROUGH WORK

HIGHER

2018 Specimen
Question Paper

National Qualifications SPECIMEN ONLY

S840/76/12

Human Biology
Paper 1 — Multiple choice

Date — Not applicable

Duration — 40 minutes

Total marks — 25

Attempt ALL questions.

You may use a calculator.

Instructions for the completion of Paper 1 are given on *Page two* of your answer booklet S840/76/02.

Record your answers on the answer grid on *Page three* of your answer booklet.

Space for rough work is provided at the end of this booklet.

Before leaving the examination room you must give your answer booklet to the Invigilator; if you do not, you may lose all the marks for this paper.

Total marks — 25

Attempt ALL questions

1. If 10% of the bases in a molecule of DNA are adenine, what is the ratio of adenine to guanine in the same molecule?

   A   1:1

   B   1:2

   C   1:3

   D   1:4

2. The following is a list of single gene mutations.

   1   Nonsense

   2   Missense

   3   Frameshift

   Which of these gene mutations is the result of a single-nucleotide substitution?

   A   1 only

   B   3 only

   C   1 and 2 only

   D   1, 2 and 3

3. The diagram shows two chromosomes, M and N, before and after a chromosomal mutation.

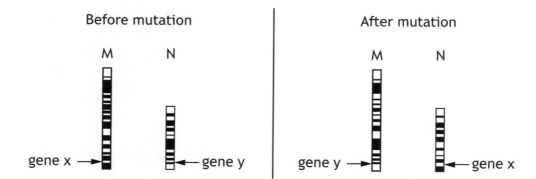

   What form of mutation has taken place?

   A   Translocation

   B   Duplication

   C   Insertion

   D   Deletion

4. Which of the following processes occurs during RNA splicing?

   A   Introns are added

   B   Exons are added

   C   Exons are removed

   D   Introns are removed

5. Metabolic pathways can be controlled by feedback inhibition where

   A   an end product binds to an enzyme found at the start of the pathway

   B   an end product binds to an enzyme found at the end of the pathway

   C   an enzyme binds to a substrate found at the start of the pathway

   D   an enzyme binds to a substrate found at the end of the pathway.

6. The diagram represents some of the processes that occur at the inner membrane of a mitochondrion.

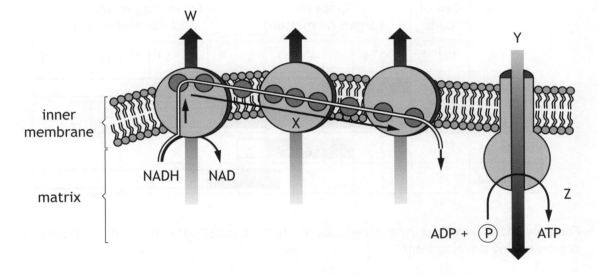

Which letter represents the flow of hydrogen ions through ATP synthase?

   A   W

   B   X

   C   Y

   D   Z

[Turn over

7. A function of the interstitial cells in the testes is to produce

   A   sperm

   B   testosterone

   C   seminal fluid

   D   follicle stimulating hormone (FSH).

8. Nicotine is a chemical that may affect antenatal development.

   The diagram shows the stages of development when major and minor malformations of organs may occur if there is exposure to nicotine.

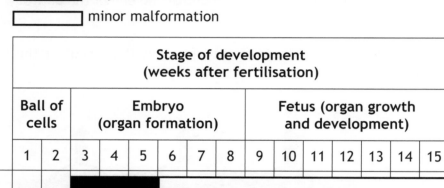

   For how many weeks during pregnancy is there a possibility of major malformations to organs during development?

   A   6

   B   7

   C   9

   D   13

9. A genetic disorder is caused by an autosomal dominant allele.

   The diagram shows the inheritance of the disorder through three generations of a family.

   Which individual confirms that this disorder is autosomal?

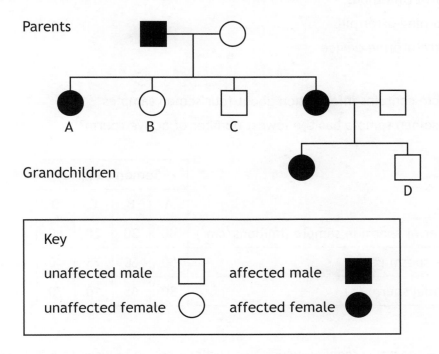

10. The following procedures can be used in the treatment of infertility.

    1   pre-implantation genetic diagnosis (PGD)

    2   intracytoplasmic sperm injection (ICSI)

    3   artificial insemination

    Which of these procedures involve *in vitro* fertilisation (IVF)?

    A   1 and 2 only

    B   1 and 3 only

    C   2 and 3 only

    D   1, 2 and 3

[Turn over

11. Which of the following forms of contraception causes thickening of the cervical mucus?

    A   Mini-pill

    B   Barrier methods

    C   Morning-after pill

    D   Intra-uterine device

12. The table contains information about four semen samples.

    Which semen sample has the lowest number of active sperm?

	Semen sample			
	A	B	C	D
Number of sperm in sample (millions/cm^3)	40	30	20	60
Active sperm (%)	50	60	75	40
Abnormal sperm (%)	30	65	10	70

13. During antenatal screening, which two techniques can be used to obtain cells for production of a karyotype?

    A   Chorionic villus sampling (CVS) and amniocentesis

    B   Amniocentesis and pre-implantation genetic diagnosis (PGD)

    C   Intra-cytoplasmic sperm injection (ICSI) and chorionic villus sampling (CVS)

    D   Pre-implantation genetic diagnosis (PGD) and intra-cytoplasmic sperm injection (ICSI)

14.   The duration of the stages in an individual's cardiac cycle are shown in the table.

Stage	Duration (s)
Diastole	0·4
Atrial systole	0·1
Ventricular systole	0·3

What is the heart rate of this individual?

A   48 beats per minute

B   75 beats per minute

C   80 beats per minute

D   150 beats per minute

15.   The diagram shows a cross-section of the heart.

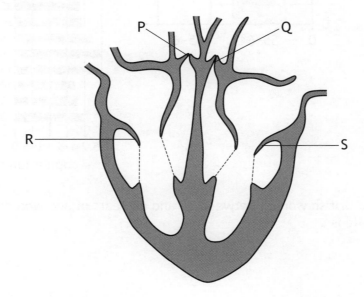

Which statement describes the movement of the valves during ventricular systole?

A   Valves P and Q open and valves R and S close.

B   Valves P and R open and valves Q and S close.

C   Valves P and Q close and valves R and S open.

D   Valves P and R close and valves Q and S open.

[Turn over

16. Which statement about lipoproteins is correct?

A   Low density lipoproteins (LDLs) transport cholesterol from body cells to the heart.

B   Low density lipoproteins (LDLs) transport cholesterol from body cells to the liver.

C   High density lipoproteins (HDLs) transport cholesterol from body cells to the heart.

D   High density lipoproteins (HDLs) transport cholesterol from body cells to the liver.

17. The graphs contain information about the population of Britain.

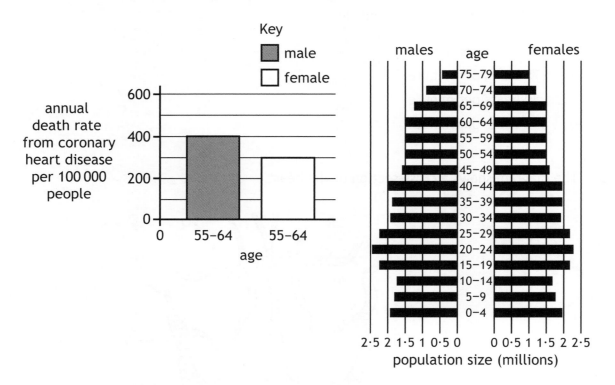

The number of British women between 55 and 64 years of age who die from coronary heart disease annually is

A   300

B   4500

C   9000

D   12 000.

18. The conversion of information into a form that memory can process is called

A   storage

B   encoding

C   retrieval

D   rehearsal.

19. By calculating body mass index (BMI), it can be determined whether an individual is obese. The table contains information about four individuals.

Individual	Height (m)	Mass (kg)
1	1·60	90
2	2·10	130
3	1·80	100
4	1·30	56

Which of these individuals would be classified as obese?

A   2 only

B   2 and 3 only

C   1, 3 and 4 only

D   1, 2, 3 and 4

20. The diagram represents a neural pathway.

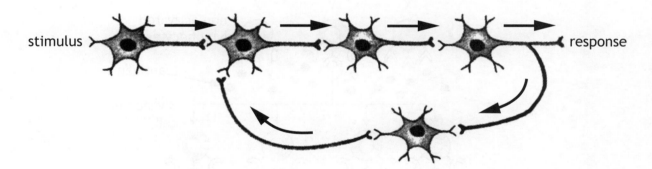

stimulus → ... → response

The type of pathway shown is a

A   sensory neural pathway

B   diverging neural pathway

C   converging neural pathway

D   reverberating neural pathway.

[Turn over

21. Which statement about the action of recreational drugs on brain neurochemistry is correct?

A   Desensitisation results from an increase in the number of neurotransmitter receptors due to the use of drugs that are agonists.

B   Desensitisation results from an increase in the number of neurotransmitter receptors due to the use of drugs that are antagonists.

C   Sensitisation results from an increase in the number of neurotransmitter receptors due to the use of drugs that are agonists.

D   Sensitisation results from an increase in the number of neurotransmitter receptors due to the use of drugs that are antagonists.

22. Which of the following is **not** part of the inflammatory response?

A   Vasodilation

B   Release of histamine

C   Production of antibodies

D   Increased capillary permeability

23. The diagram represents the production of a clonal population of lymphocytes.

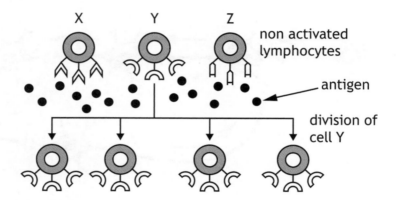

The division of cell Y is stimulated by

A   the presence of lymphocytes X and Z

B   the presence of an antigen in the blood

C   the binding of antibodies to receptors on the cell membrane

D   the binding of antigens to receptors on the cell membrane.

24. Two groups of subjects were used when carrying out clinical trials of a vaccine.

One group was given the vaccine, while the other group was given a placebo.

The purpose of the placebo was to

A   reduce experimental error

B   ensure a valid comparison

C   allow a statistical analysis of the results

D   ensure that researchers are unaware who has been vaccinated.

25. The table contains information about the number of influenza cases over five years.

Year	Number of influenza cases in January	Number of influenza cases in July
2001	580	120
2002	620	345
2003	1200	350
2004	120	145
2005	400	100

Which of the following conclusions can be drawn from the data in the table?

A   There are always more influenza cases in January than in July.

B   The number of influenza cases decreased by 75% between January and July of 2005.

C   The greatest percentage decrease in influenza cases occurred between January and July of 2003.

D   The greatest percentage increase in influenza cases occurred between July 2002 and January 2003.

[END OF SPECIMEN QUESTION PAPER]

SPACE FOR ROUGH WORK

SPACE FOR ROUGH WORK

[BLANK PAGE]

DO NOT WRITE ON THIS PAGE

H

National Qualifications
SPECIMEN ONLY

Mark

S840/76/02

Human Biology
Paper 1 — Multiple choice
Answer booklet

Date — Not applicable

Duration — 40 minutes

Fill in these boxes and read what is printed below.

Full name of centre

Town

Forename(s)

Surname

Number of seat

Date of birth

Day   Month   Year   Scottish candidate number

Instructions for the completion of Paper 1 are given on *Page two*.

Record your answers on the answer grid on *Page three*.

You may use a calculator.

Use **blue** or **black** ink.

Before leaving the examination room you must give your answer booklet to the Invigilator; if you do not, you may lose all the marks for this paper.

Paper 1 — 25 marks

The questions for Paper 1 are contained in the question paper S840/76/12.

Read these and record your answers on the answer grid on *Page three*.

Use **blue** or **black** ink. Do NOT use gel pens or pencil.

1.   The answer to each question is **either** A, B, C or D. Decide what your answer is, then fill in the appropriate bubble (see sample question below).

2.   There is **only one correct** answer to each question.

3.   Any rough working should be done on the space for rough work at the end of the question paper S840/76/12.

Sample question

The digestive enzyme pepsin is most active in the

    A   mouth

    B   stomach

    C   duodenum

    D   pancreas.

The correct answer is **B** — stomach. The answer **B** bubble has been clearly filled in (see below).

Changing an answer

If you decide to change your answer, cancel your first answer by putting a cross through it (see below) and fill in the answer you want. The answer below has been changed to **D**.

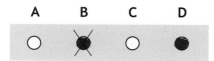

If you then decide to change back to an answer you have already scored out, put a tick (✓) to the **right** of the answer you want, as shown below:

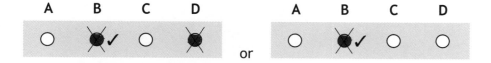

Paper 1 — Answer grid

	A	B	C	D
1	○	○	○	○
2	○	○	○	○
3	○	○	○	○
4	○	○	○	○
5	○	○	○	○
6	○	○	○	○
7	○	○	○	○
8	○	○	○	○
9	○	○	○	○
10	○	○	○	○
11	○	○	○	○
12	○	○	○	○
13	○	○	○	○
14	○	○	○	○
15	○	○	○	○
16	○	○	○	○
17	○	○	○	○
18	○	○	○	○
19	○	○	○	○
20	○	○	○	○
21	○	○	○	○
22	○	○	○	○
23	○	○	○	○
24	○	○	○	○
25	○	○	○	○

[BLANK PAGE]

DO NOT WRITE ON THIS PAGE

National Qualifications
SPECIMEN ONLY

S840/76/01

Human Biology
Paper 2

Mark

Date — Not applicable

Duration — 2 hours 20 minutes

Fill in these boxes and read what is printed below.

Full name of centre

Town

Forename(s)

Surname

Number of seat

Date of birth

Day	Month	Year	Scottish candidate number

Total marks — 95

Attempt ALL questions.

You may use a calculator.

Question 17 contains a choice.

Write your answers clearly in the spaces provided in this booklet. Additional space for answers and rough work is provided at the end of this booklet. If you use this space you must clearly identify the question number you are attempting. Any rough work must be written in this booklet. Score through your rough work when you have written your final copy.

Use **blue** or **black** ink.

Before leaving the examination room you must give this booklet to the Invigilator; if you do not, you may lose all the marks for this paper.

MARKS | DO NOT WRITE IN THIS MARGIN

Total marks — 95

Attempt ALL questions

Question 17 contains a choice

1. The human body contains many specialised cells, all of which have developed from embryonic stem cells.

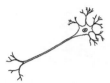

nerve cells   liver cells   cardiac muscle cells

(a) Name the process by which a stem cell develops into a specialised body cell and explain how this process occurs.   **2**

Process _____

Explanation _____

_____

(b) The nucleus of a germline stem cell divides twice during meiosis.

Describe what happens to chromosomes during each division.   **2**

First division _____

_____

Second division _____

_____

(c) A company has developed a drug that could be used to treat the symptoms of an inherited disease. Before proceeding to clinical trials using volunteers, the company decides to carry out additional tests in the laboratory using embryonic stem cells.

Suggest **one** ethical consideration that might have influenced this decision to use embryonic stem cells.   **1**

_____

_____

MARKS | DO NOT WRITE IN THIS MARGIN

2. The diagram shows stages in the synthesis of a polypeptide.

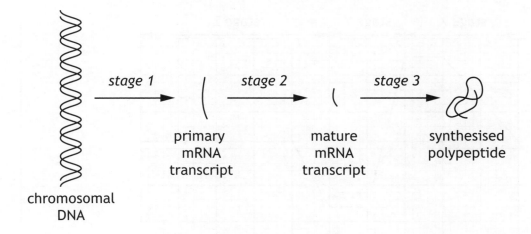

chromosomal DNA

(a) Name the enzyme that catalyses stage 1 of this process.   1

_____

(b) State the exact location within the cell where stage 3 occurs.   1

_____

(c) (i) Explain why the primary mRNA transcript is so much shorter than chromosomal DNA.   1

_____

_____

    (ii) Explain why the mature mRNA transcript is shorter than the primary mRNA transcript.   1

_____

_____

[Turn over

MARKS | DO NOT WRITE IN THIS MARGIN

3. The graph shows how the temperature of a reaction tube is changed during one cycle of the polymerase chain reaction (PCR).

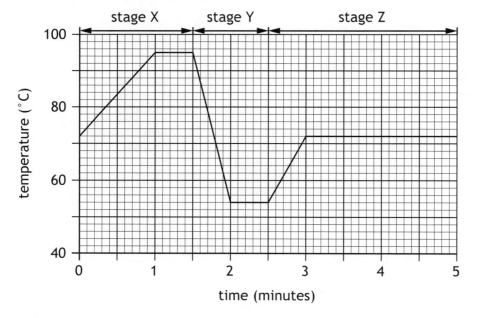

(a) State the maximum change in temperature that the reaction tube experiences during one cycle of PCR.   **1**

_____ °C

(b) State the function of PCR.   **1**

_____

_____

(c) Describe what happens to the DNA during stage X.   **1**

_____

_____

(d) Short sections of DNA called primers are involved in stage Y.

Describe what happens to these primers during stage Y.   **1**

_____

_____

MARKS | DO NOT WRITE IN THIS MARGIN

3. (continued)

(e) Suggest why the temperature is increased during stage Z.

1

_____

_____

(f) A forensic scientist discovered a tiny spot of blood at a crime scene.

A sample taken from this spot contained 10 molecules of DNA.

The sample underwent PCR cycles for 30 minutes.

Use data from the graph to calculate how many molecules of DNA would be present after this time.

1

Space for calculation

_____ molecules

[Turn over

4. An experiment was carried out to investigate the effect of substrate concentration on the production of an end-product in an enzyme controlled reaction.

The enzyme urease was used, which breaks down urea into ammonia.

$$urea \xrightarrow{\text{urease}} ammonia$$

Urease and urea solutions were mixed together and added to test tubes containing agar jelly as shown in the diagram.

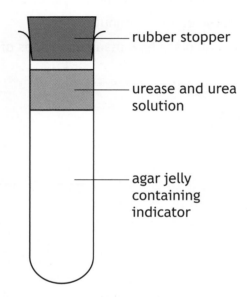

- rubber stopper

- urease and urea solution

- agar jelly containing indicator

Five different concentrations of urea solution were added.

During the reaction the ammonia produced diffused through the agar jelly, changing the indicator from yellow to blue.

The length of the agar jelly stained blue was measured after the experiment had been allowed to run for 48 hours.

The results of the experiment are shown in the table.

Urea concentration added (moles)	Average length of agar stained blue (mm)
0·03	2
0·06	4
0·13	8
0·25	16
0·50	32

MARKS | DO NOT WRITE IN THIS MARGIN

4. **(continued)**

(a) Draw a line graph to show the results of the experiment.

(Additional graph paper, if required, can be found on *Page twenty-seven*.)

2

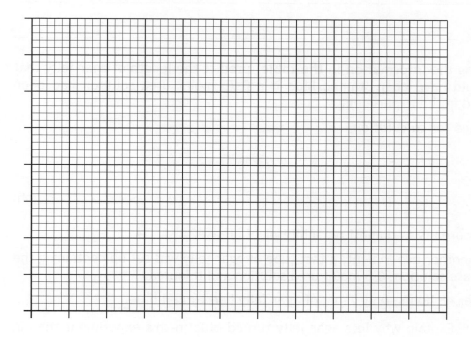

(b) (i) Name **one** variable that should be controlled when setting up this experiment.

1

_____

(ii) Name **one** variable that should be kept constant during the 48 hours of this experiment.

1

_____

(c) Give the feature of this experiment that makes the results reliable.

1

_____

_____

(d) Explain why the test tubes were left for 48 hours before the results were obtained.

1

_____

_____

MARKS | DO NOT WRITE IN THIS MARGIN

4. **(continued)**

(e) State **one** conclusion that can be drawn from the results of this experiment.   1

_____

_____

(f) Using the **information in the table**, predict the length of agar jelly that would have been stained blue if a 0·75 molar urea solution had been used in the experiment.   1

Space for calculation

_____ mm

(g) Thiourea is a competitive inhibitor of urease.

In another experiment, a test tube of agar jelly was set up containing the urease solution, 0·5 molar urea solution and thiourea.

After 48 hours, only 7 mm of agar jelly had turned blue.

  (i) Explain why less agar jelly turned blue in this experiment than in the first experiment, which also used a 0·5 molar urea solution.   1

_____

_____

  (ii) Suggest why some agar jelly turned blue in this experiment.   1

_____

_____

MARKS | DO NOT WRITE IN THIS MARGIN

5. The diagram represents the glycolysis stage of respiration in a muscle cell.

$$\text{glucose} \xrightarrow{\textit{phase 1}} \text{intermediate compounds} \xrightarrow{\textit{phase 2}} \text{pyruvate}$$

(a) Phase 1 is the energy investment stage of glycolysis while phase 2 is the energy pay-off stage of glycolysis.

Describe what happens during the energy investment and energy pay-off phases of glycolysis.

2

Energy investment phase _____

_____

Energy pay-off phase _____

_____

(b) Once pyruvate has been formed it can be converted into two different compounds, depending on the conditions.

Name **one** of these compounds and state under what conditions it would be produced.

2

Name _____

Conditions _____

_____

(c) Most human muscle tissue contains a mixture of fast and slow twitch muscle fibres.

Complete the table to show differences between these two types of muscle fibre.

2

	Fast twitch	Slow twitch
Generation of ATP	from glycolysis	
Major storage fuel		fats

[Turn over

MARKS

6.   Sickle cell disease is an autosomal blood disorder in which a faulty form of haemoglobin, called haemoglobin S, is produced. This protein is an inefficient carrier of oxygen.

The allele for normal haemoglobin (H) is incompletely dominant to the allele for haemoglobin S (S).

Heterozygous individuals (HS) suffer from a milder condition called sickle cell trait.

The chart shows the incidence of these conditions in three generations of a family.

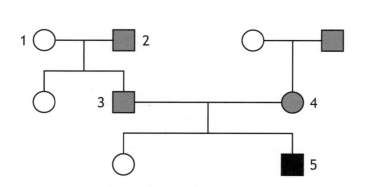

Key

■ male with sickle cell trait

■ male with sickle cell disease

○ unaffected female

● female with sickle cell trait

(a)   State the genotype of individual 5.   1

_____

(b)   Individuals 3 and 4 go on to have a third child.

State the percentage chance that this child will have the same genotype as the parents.   1

Space for working

_____ %

(c)   Sickle cell disease is caused by a substitution mutation in the gene that codes for haemoglobin.

(i)   Describe how this form of mutation affects the structure of the gene.   1

_____

_____

(ii)   Explain how this might change the structure of a protein such as haemoglobin.   1

_____

_____

MARKS | DO NOT WRITE IN THIS MARGIN

6. (continued)

(d) During IVF treatment, it is possible to detect single gene disorders in fertilised eggs before they are implanted into the mother.

Give the term that describes this procedure.

1

_____

(e) It has been discovered that the gene that codes for fetal haemoglobin is unaffected by the substitution mutation that causes sickle cell disease.

This gene is 'switched off' at birth.

Use this information to suggest how a drug designed to treat sickle cell disease in young children could function.

1

_____

_____

[Turn over

MARKS | DO NOT WRITE IN THIS MARGIN

7. The graph shows how the plasma concentration of oestrogen and the thickness of the endometrium vary during a woman's menstrual cycle.

Key
——o—— oestrogen concentration
– – x – – thickness of endometrium

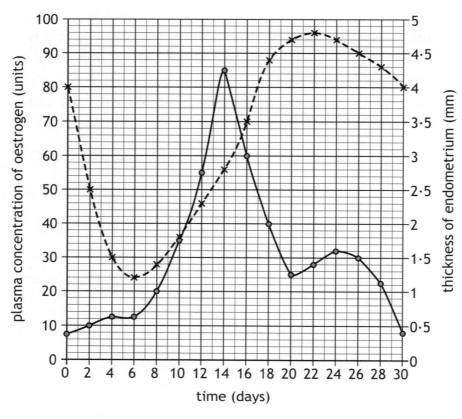

(a) (i) State the plasma concentration of oestrogen on day 12 of this cycle.   1

_____ units

(ii) Describe how the pituitary gland stimulates the change in the plasma concentration of oestrogen between days 6 and 14.   2

_____

_____

_____

_____

MARKS | DO NOT WRITE IN THIS MARGIN

7. (continued)

(b) Calculate the percentage increase in the thickness of the endometrium between day 6 and day 22. **1**

Space for calculation

____________ %

(c) Explain why the thickness of the endometrium decreases after day 22 of this cycle. **1**

____

____

(d) Describe **one** way that ovulatory drugs stimulate ovulation. **1**

____

____

[Turn over

MARKS | DO NOT WRITE IN THIS MARGIN

8. The diagram represents a section through an artery.

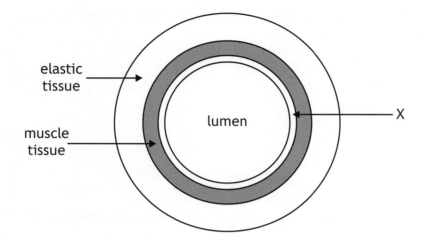

(a) Name layer X.   1

_____

(b) Describe how the presence of muscle tissue in the artery wall helps to control the flow of blood around the body.   1

_____

_____

(c) Describe how an atheroma forming under layer X may lead to the formation of a blood clot and state the possible effects of this.   5

_____

_____

_____

_____

_____

_____

_____

_____

_____

_____

MARKS | DO NOT WRITE IN THIS MARGIN

9. The graph shows how an individual's heart rate and stroke volume changed as their oxygen uptake increased during exercise.

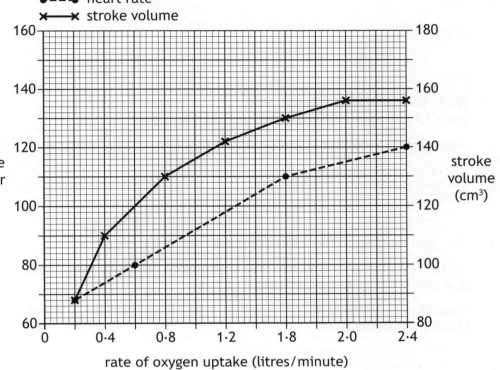

Key
•---• heart rate
✗——✗ stroke volume

(a) (i) State the individual's heart rate when the rate of oxygen uptake was 1·2 litres/minute.

1

_____

(ii) Using data from the graph, describe how the stroke volume changed as oxygen uptake increased.

1

_____

_____

_____

(iii) State the stroke volume when the heart rate was 110 beats per minute.

1

_____ cm³

[Turn over

MARKS | DO NOT WRITE IN THIS MARGIN

9. (continued)

(b) Calculate the cardiac output when the rate of oxygen uptake was 2·4 litres per minute.

Space for calculation

_____ litres/min

(c) (i) When the individual's blood pressure was measured an hour after exercise, a reading of 140/90 mmHg was recorded.

Describe what the **first** figure in a blood pressure reading represents.

1

_____

_____

(ii) The individual was diagnosed as having high blood pressure.

One of the effects of this was that their ankles regularly swelled up due to a build-up of tissue fluid.

Suggest why there is a link between high blood pressure and the build-up of tissue fluid.

2

_____

_____

_____

_____

MARKS | DO NOT WRITE IN THIS MARGIN

10. The graph shows changes in blood glucose concentration in a diabetic and a non-diabetic individual after each had consumed a glucose drink.

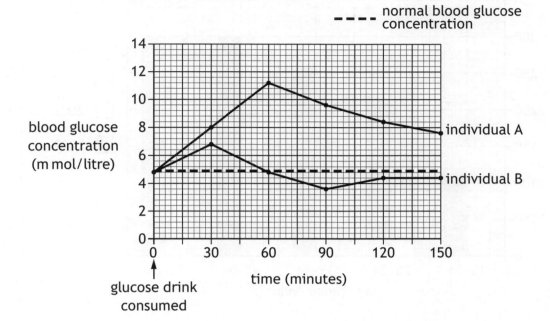

(a) (i) Describe how the graph indicates that individual B is **not** a diabetic.   1

_____

_____

(ii) **Use data from the graph** to describe the changes that occur in the blood glucose concentration of individual A after consuming the glucose drink.   2

_____

_____

_____

_____

(b) Describe the role of insulin in the development of type 1 and type 2 diabetes.   2

Type 1 _____

_____

Type 2 _____

_____

MARKS | DO NOT WRITE IN THIS MARGIN

11. The graph shows data on obesity for a European country in 2003 and 2012.

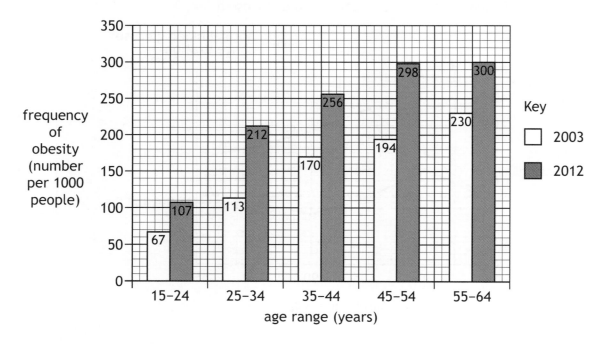

(a) (i) Describe **two** general trends shown in the graph.   2

1 _____

_____

2 _____

_____

(ii) In 2012 the number of people in this country aged 35 to 44 was 6 million.

Calculate how many people aged 35 to 44 were obese.   1

Space for calculation

Number of people _____

(b) State **one** piece of advice that an obese individual would be given to adapt their diet or lifestyle in order to avoid long-term health problems.   1

_____

_____

MARKS | DO NOT WRITE IN THIS MARGIN

12. An investigation was carried out into how the meaning of words affects the recall of lists from long-term memory.

Two groups of 20 people were each shown a list of five words and asked to study them for 30 seconds.

Group 1 was shown words that all had a similar meaning, while group 2 was shown words that had different meanings.

Words shown to group 1 — *large, big, great, huge, wide.*

Words shown to group 2 — *late, cheap, rare, bright, rough.*

After reading a book for an hour, the groups were asked to write down the words that were on their list.

The results of the investigation are shown in the table.

Group	Meaning of words shown	Number of people who correctly recalled all the words
1	similar	11
2	different	17

(a) Describe **two** ways that the investigators could minimise variation between the two groups of people.   2

1 _____

_____

2 _____

_____

(b) Suggest why the groups were asked to read a book for an hour.   1

_____

_____

(c) State a conclusion that can be drawn from the results of the investigation.   1

_____

_____

[Turn over

MARKS | DO NOT WRITE IN THIS MARGIN

13. The diagram shows how the immune system responds to polio viruses in a vaccine.

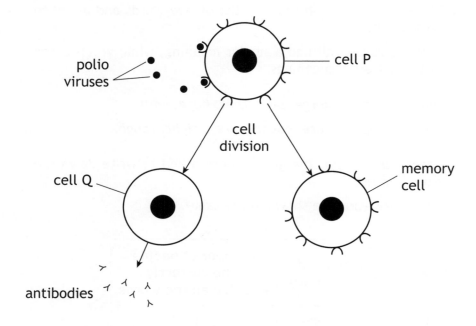

(a) Describe how a polio virus is able to attach to cell P.   1

_____

_____

(b) Name cell Q.   1

_____

(c) Describe the role of memory cells in the immune system.   1

_____

_____

(d) Explain why vaccination against polio would **not** provide immunity against the influenza virus.   1

_____

_____

(e) Clinical trials of vaccines often use a double-blind protocol.

Describe what is meant by the term double-blind.   1

_____

_____

MARKS | DO NOT WRITE IN THIS MARGIN

14. The graph shows the number of whooping cough cases over a 65 year period in a country.

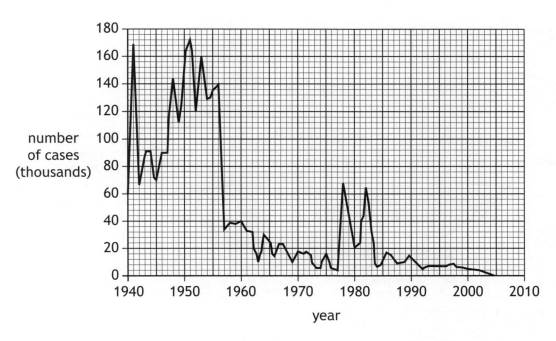

(a) (i) Using information from the graph, state the year in which a vaccine for whooping cough was introduced.

1

_____

(ii) Suggest a reason for the unexpected increase in the number of cases of whooping cough in 1977.

1

_____

_____

(b) The number of cases of whooping cough decreases to a very low level after 2000 because of herd immunity.

Explain what is meant by the term 'herd immunity'.

2

_____

_____

_____

_____

[Turn over

MARKS | DO NOT WRITE IN THIS MARGIN

15. The following figures contain information about the causes of death and survival rates in two countries, A and B, in 2010.

Figure 1 — Causes of death in countries A and B during 2010

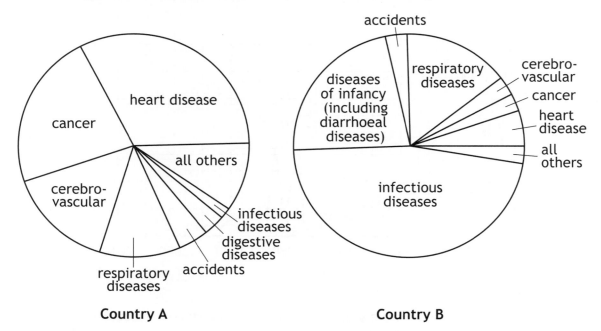

Country A   **Country B**

Figure 2 — Percentage survival rates in countries A and B in 2010

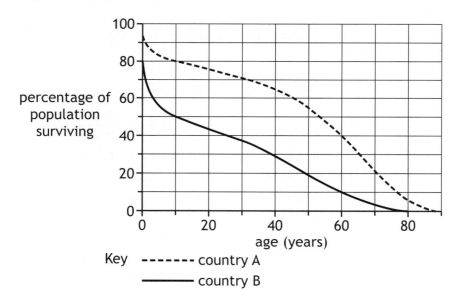

(a) Use information from **Figure 2** to explain the lower incidence of heart disease in country B.

1

_____

_____

MARKS | DO NOT WRITE IN THIS MARGIN

15.   (continued)

(b)   (i)   Calculate the percentage of the population of country A that die before the age of 10.   1

Space for calculation

_____ %

(ii)   In 1950 three million babies were born in country B.

Calculate how many of these individuals were still alive in 2010, assuming no migration occurred.   1

Space for calculation

_____

(c)   Suggest **one** reason why a widespread vaccination programme against infectious diseases might **not** be possible in country B.   1

_____

_____

[Turn over

MARKS DO NOT WRITE IN THIS MARGIN

16. Pulmonary tuberculosis (TB) is an infectious disease of the lungs caused by a bacterium.

This bacterium can also damage other organs in the body. When this happens it is called non-pulmonary TB.

The table shows the number of reported cases of pulmonary and non-pulmonary TB in Scotland between 1981 and 2006.

Year	Number of cases of pulmonary TB	Number of cases of non-pulmonary TB
1981	659	140
1986	500	178
1991	452	97
1996	408	102
2001	275	125
2006	255	153

(a) (i) Calculate in which five year period the greatest decrease in the total number of cases of TB occurred.

Space for calculation

1

_____

(ii) Compare the trend in the number of cases of pulmonary TB with that of non-pulmonary TB between 1991 and 2006.

1

_____

_____

(iii) Calculate, as a simple whole number ratio, the number of cases of pulmonary TB compared to non-pulmonary TB in 2001.

Space for calculation

1

_____ : _____
pulmonary TB   non-pulmonary TB

(b) Non-pulmonary TB is often associated with HIV infection.

Suggest a reason for this association.

1

_____

_____

MARKS | DO NOT WRITE IN THIS MARGIN

17. Attempt **either** A **or** B. Write your answer in the space below and on *Page twenty-six*.

A   Describe the autonomic nervous system (ANS) and how it affects heart rate and digestive processes.   **8**

OR

B   Describe how neurotransmitters relay impulses across the synapse.   **8**

You may use labelled diagrams where appropriate.

MARKS

ADDITIONAL SPACE FOR ANSWER to question 17

[END OF SPECIMEN QUESTION PAPER]

MARKS | DO NOT WRITE IN THIS MARGIN

ADDITIONAL SPACE FOR ANSWERS AND ROUGH WORK

Additional graph paper for question 4 (a)

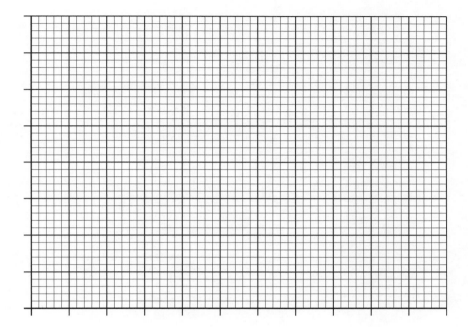

ADDITIONAL SPACE FOR ANSWERS AND ROUGH WORK

HIGHER

Answers

SQA HIGHER
HUMAN BIOLOGY 2018

HIGHER HUMAN BIOLOGY 2017

Section 1

Question	Answer	Mark
1.	C	1
2.	D	1
3.	A	1
4.	C	1
5.	A	1
6.	B	1
7.	C	1
8.	A	1
9.	A	1
10.	C	1
11.	C	1
12.	B	1
13.	D	1
14.	B	1
15.	B	1
16.	C	1
17.	D	1
18.	B	1
19.	D	1
20.	D	1

Section 2

Question			Expected answer(s)	Max Mark
1.	(a)		Mitosis	1
	(b)		Connective	1
	(c)		The gene(s) coding for haemoglobin is switched on/expressed in the red blood cell but is switched off/not expressed in the white blood cell.	1
	(d)		Cell divides excessively/unregulated division occurs. OR Cell does not respond to regulatory signals.	1
	(e)	(i)	15	1
		(ii)	0·1	1
2.	(a)	(i)	One nucleotide/base is replaced with another.	1
		(ii)	One amino acid is changed/the sequence of amino acids is changed. OR The enzyme is shorter due to the presence of a stop codon.	1

Question			Expected answer(s)	Max Mark
	(b)	(i)	Phenylalanine cannot be broken down/converted (to tyrosine). OR Enzyme 1 does not break down phenylalanine/lead to the production of tyrosine.	1
		(ii)	They get tyrosine from their diet.	1
	(c)	(i)	Post-natal (screening)	1
		(ii)	Restricted diet/low phenylalanine diet	1
	(d)		25	1
3.	(a)		To allow (time for) the reaction to take place/phenolphthalein to be produced/substrate to be broken down. OR So the enzyme/phosphatase is not denatured. OR So the enzyme/phosphatase can work at its optimum pH.	1
	(b)		1. Concentration of inhibitor/alkali/enzyme/phosphatase. 2. Type of alkali. 3. Temperature of solutions/test tubes. 4. pH of solutions/test tubes/alkali. *Any 2 points for 2 marks*	2
	(c)		Axes have correct scales and labels. *1 mark* Points correctly plotted and line drawn. *1 mark*	2

Concentration of substrate (M)	Absorbance (units)
0.05	0.20
0.10	0.30
0.20	0.48
0.40	0.64
0.60	0.78
0.80	0.90

Question			Expected answer(s)	Max Mark
	(d)		As the substrate concentration increases there is an increase in absorbance/intensity of colour. *1 mark* This indicates that more phenolphthalein/product has been produced. OR This indicates that there is greater enzyme activity. *1 mark*	2
	(e)		The absorbance levels will remain low/lower/not increase/increase less (at each substrate concentration).	1
4.	(a)	(i)	Oestrogen stimulates/causes the production/triggers the release of LH.	1
		(ii)	3·1	1

Question			Expected answer(s)	Max Mark
	(b)	(i)	1:4	1
		(ii)	Endometrium thickness continues to increase after oestrogen concentration decreases (between day 14 and day 20).	1
	(c)		Endometrium thickness would not fall/not decrease/remain high/stay above 4·5. OR Oestrogen concentration would remain constant/stay the same/stay around 30 units/would not decrease/remain high.	1
	(d)		Fertility drugs prevent the negative feedback effect of <u>oestrogen</u>. OR Fertility drugs mimic the action of <u>FSH/LH</u>. OR Fertility drugs stimulate the production of <u>FSH/LH</u>.	1
5.	(a)	(i)	Artery/arteriole	1
		(ii)	Vasoconstriction/contraction/constriction. OR Narrowing of the lumen/cavity/channel.	1
	(b)	(i)	Endothelium/epithelium/endothelial/epithelial	1
		(ii)	Pressure forces substances out/through the capillary wall. OR By pressure filtration.	1
		(iii)	Proteins	1
	(c)		Absorbs (excess) tissue fluid. OR Returns lymph/tissue fluid to the blood/circulatory system.	1
6.	(a)		Systolic is when the heart beats/contracts/constricts <u>and</u> diastolic is when the heart relaxes/rests/does not beat.	1
	(b)		(It/the cuff/pressure) squeezes/closes/squashes/compresses the artery/vessel. OR (It/the cuff/pressure) cuts off/restricts/prevents blood flow/circulation.	1
	(c)	(i)	Fatty material/cholesterol/fibrous material/calcium builds up. OR An atheroma/plaque forms. *1 mark* Diameter of lumen/cavity/channel of <u>artery</u> reduced. OR Loss of elasticity in <u>arterial</u> wall. *1 mark*	2
		(ii)	The <u>cholesterol</u> level/concentration increases in the arteries/vessels/blood/endothelium. OR Less <u>cholesterol</u> is removed from the arteries/vessels/blood/is taken to the liver.	1

Question			Expected answer(s)	Max Mark
7.	(a)		The number of cases (of pulmonary embolism) increases with age. *1 mark* The number of cases is higher in women taking HRT compared to those taking the placebo/not taking HRT. *1 mark*	2
	(b)		The difference in cases between taking HRT or the placebo is not large/may not be significant. OR There are only a small number of cases compared to the large sample size/from 12 000 women.	1
	(c)		(Differences in) diet/smoking/degree of exercise/level of cholesterol/blood pressure/genes/weight/drugs/medication/alcohol/diabetes/high blood pressure/obesity.	1
	(d)		They used a large sample size/12 000 women/large groups/groups of 4000 women.	1
	(e)	(i)	Between the ages of 10 and 35 average bone mass increased and then it decreased between 35 and 80. *1 mark* It increased from 50% to 100%/by 50%. OR It decreased from 100% to 46%/by 54%. *1 mark*	2
		(ii)	Any value from 37 to 38	1
8.	(a)		Mitochondrion/mitochondria	1
	(b)		1. <u>Vesicle</u> fuses with membrane/releases neurotransmitter. 2. <u>Neurotransmitter</u> diffuses/moves across the gap/synaptic cleft/synapse. 3. Neurotransmitter binds to/joins with the <u>receptor</u>. 4. Sufficient/a minimum amount of neurotransmitter is required (to transmit impulse). *Any 3 points for 3 marks*	3
	(c)		Effect — increased number of/sensitivity of receptors. Consequence — leads to addiction.	2
9.	(a)		Medulla	1
	(b)		They cause opposite effects/work against each other. OR The sympathetic speeds up heart (rate) <u>and</u> the parasympathetic slows down heart (rate).	1
	(c)	(i)	58	1
		(ii)	32	1
	(d)		The <u>SAN</u> controls the heart (rate/beat)/acts as a pacemaker/still sends impulses (to the AVN)/is auto rhythmic.	1

Question			Expected answer(s)	Max Mark
	(e)		There is a greater change (from the resting rate) when the parasympathetic nerve is blocked (compared to when the sympathetic is blocked). **OR** Blockage of the parasympathetic nerve raises heart rate by 18/32 (beats) while blockage of the sympathetic nerve lowers it by 14 (beats).	1
	(f)		It increases breathing rate. **OR** It decreases digestive processes/ digestion/peristalsis.	1
10.	(a)		Antigens	1
	(b)		<u>Phagocytosis</u> is carried out on the <u>pathogen</u>. **OR** <u>Pathogen</u> is engulfed/captured by phagocyte <u>and</u> broken down. *1 mark* Phagocyte displays (fragments of) antigen/X (on the surface/membrane). **OR** Phagocyte becomes an antigen-presenting cell. *1 mark*	2
	(c)		Cytokines	1
	(d)		Allows a faster/greater response to the same pathogen/antigen/infection. **OR** Individual does not develop the same infection again.	1
	(e)		It survives/hides within <u>phagocytic cells/phagocytes</u>.	1
11.	(a)	(i)	85·71/85·7/86	1
		(ii)	1921—1951	1
		(iii)	1. Development or availability of vaccines/immunisation/establishment of herd immunity. 2. Improvement in water supply/ chlorination of drinking water. 3. Improved sanitation/waste disposal systems/hygiene/housing/living conditions. 4. Improved storage/handling/ availability/production of food/diet. 5. Improved health care/medical facilities/medical treatments/ medicines/drug therapy/antisepsis/ sexual health. *Any 2 points for 2 marks*	2
	(b)	(i)	78, 78, 78	1
		(ii)	(In 1861) a large number of deaths occurred in childhood. **OR** (In 1861) there was large childhood/ infant mortality. **OR** Individuals have survived childhood. **OR** Individuals have survived/avoided illnesses/diseases (in childhood).	1

Question		Expected answer(s)	Max Mark
12.	A	**Structure** 1. DNA is composed of nucleotides containing deoxyribose (sugar), phosphate and base. 2. There is a sugar phosphate backbone. 3. The four bases are adenine, thymine, cytosine and guanine. 4. Cytosine bonds/pairs with guanine and adenine bonds with thymine. 5. Bases/two strands are joined by hydrogen bonds. 6. Strands are anti-parallel/run in opposite directions/3′ to 5′ and 5′ to 3′. 7. DNA/two strands form a double helix (shape). **Replication** a) DNA/double helix is unwound/ unzipped. b) A primer is needed at the start of replication/attaches to DNA strand. c) DNA polymerase adds nucleotides to the 3′ end (of a new/growing strand/ primer). d) One strand is replicated continuously and the other strand is replicated in fragments/discontinuously. e) The strand replicated in fragments is joined together by ligase.	9
	B	**Structure** 1. RNA is single stranded. 2. It is composed of nucleotides containing ribose (sugar), phosphate and base. 3. The four bases are uracil, adenine, cytosine and guanine. 4. Groups of three bases/nucleotides form codons in mRNA/anticodons in tRNA. 5. Start/stop codons exist. 6. tRNA folds due to base pairing/has an attachment site for a specific amino acid. 7. rRNA (and protein) forms a ribosome. **Transcription** a) Transcription occurs in the nucleus. b) RNA polymerase forms mRNA/unwinds and unzips DNA. c) (Complementary) base pairing occurs — adenine with uracil, guanine with cytosine. d) The primary transcript/mRNA contains introns and exons. e) Introns are removed/exons remain after (RNA) splicing. f) (Splicing) forms the mature transcript/mRNA.	9

HIGHER HUMAN BIOLOGY 2018

Section 1

Question	Answer	Mark
1.	B	1
2.	A	1
3.	B	1
4.	D	1
5.	B	1
6.	D	1
7.	C	1
8.	A	1
9.	A	1
10.	C	1
11.	D	1
12.	D	1
13.	C	1
14.	B	1
15.	C	1
16.	A	1
17.	B	1
18.	D	1
19.	D	1
20.	C	1

Section 2

Question			Expected response	Max Mark
1.	(a)	(i)	Cytoplasm	1
		(ii)	(Two) ATP (molecules) are used. OR ATP provides phosphate (to phosphorylate glucose/intermediates). OR Phosphorylation of glucose/intermediates occur.	1
	(b)	(i)	NADH/NADH+ (Accept NADH$_2$)	1
		(ii)	NAD allows ATP production (during glycolysis). OR NAD allows glycolysis to continue. OR NAD accepts/collects/carries hydrogen/hydrogen ions. OR NAD allows dehydrogenase enzymes to function.	1
		(iii)	Not enough/no oxygen (reaches the muscle cells).	1
2.	(a)		Any **two** from: • mass/weight/surface area/size/type of liver; • volume of inhibitor/alcohol/solution; • initial alcohol concentration; • pH of solution; • type of alcohol/inhibitor.	2

Question			Expected response	Max Mark
	(b)		It binds elsewhere (on the enzyme)/the allosteric site/not to the active site and changes the shape of the active site.	1
	(c)	(i)	Axes have correct scales and labels. (1) Points correctly plotted and line drawn. (1)	2

Inhibitor concentration (mM)	Final alcohol concentration (% of initial concentration)
0·5	20
1·5	28
2·5	60
3·5	96
4·5	100
5·5	100

Question			Expected response	Max Mark
		(ii)	As inhibitor concentration increases (enzyme) activity decreases. (1) Beyond 4·5 (mM) there is no (enzyme) activity/activity stops/activity levels off/activity remains constant. (1)	2
	(d)		The (final) alcohol concentration will not change/will not decrease/will stay at 100%/will remain high. OR (Increasing the initial) alcohol/substrate concentration will have no effect (on the results).	1
3.	(a)	(i)	Deletion	1
		(ii)	The order/sequence of amino acids would change OR Amino acids after the mutation would change OR The protein is shorter due to the presence of a stop codon.	1
	(b)		Systematics	1
	(c)	(i)	15 : 5 : 1	1
		(ii)	The more an animal has the better is its sense of smell. OR Rats have the best/a better sense of smell because they have most (functional genes/nasal receptors). OR Chickens have the worst/a poorer sense of smell because they have fewest (functional genes/nasal receptors).	1

Question			Expected response	Max Mark
	(d)		1. <u>Deletion</u> is the loss of part of a chromosome/genes. 2. <u>Duplication</u> is the repeat of a part of a chromosome/genes. OR <u>Duplication</u> — the breaking off of part of a chromosome/genes and it reattaching to its homologous partner. 3. <u>Translocation</u> the moving/swapping/transfer of parts of chromosomes/genes to another chromosome/non-homologous chromosome. *Any 2 from 3* 4. These mutations/changes can be lethal/be fatal to/kill the individual/life threatening. **OR** An example named such as cri-du-chat for deletion, myeloid leukaemia or <u>familial</u> Down's syndrome for translocation. **(1)**	3
4.	(a)	(i)	5·6 <u>per 100 000</u>	1
		(ii)	37·5	1
		(iii)	46	1
		(iv)	Between <u>2007 and 2009</u> there is an increase in breastfeeding while infant mortality continues to increase/does not decrease. (Accept 2007 and 2008 **or** 2008 and 2009 as an alternative to between 2007 and 2009.)	1
	(b)	(i)	6	1
		(ii)	Bottles/water/milk can be contaminated with <u>bacteria</u>/<u>viruses</u>/<u>pathogens</u>/<u>microbes</u>. **OR** Breastfed babies can get <u>antibodies</u>/<u>immunity</u> from their mother.	1
5.	(a)		Medulla **(1)** SAN/right atrium (wall)/pacemaker **(1)**	2
	(b)		Sympathetic nervous system increases heart rate while parasympathetic system decreases it. **(1)** Sympathetic system releases/produces noradrenaline/norepinephrine while the parasympathetic system releases/produces acetylcholine. **(1)**	2
	(c)	(i)	60	1
		(ii)	<u>Ventricles</u> are contracting/pumping blood/<u>ventricular</u> systole. **OR** Impulses are spreading through the <u>ventricles</u>.	1
6.	(a)		15—44	1
	(b)	(i)	Statins	1
		(ii)	2007/2008	1

Question			Expected response	Max Mark
	(c)		Component of the cell membrane. **OR** Used to synthesise steroids/sex hormones/testosterone/oestrogen/progesterone.	1
7.	(a)	(i)	30·68/30·7/31	1
		(ii)	The office worker has/they have less muscle/more fat. **OR** The swimmer has more muscle/less fat. (Accept 'bigger muscles' or more muscular.)	1
	(b)		Cells/receptors have become less sensitive/(more) resistant/desensitised to insulin. **OR** Cells have less insulin receptors. **(1)** This means that glucose cannot enter the cells. **OR** This means that glucose cannot be converted to/stored as glycogen. **OR** This means less glucose is converted to/stored as glycogen **(1)** (Accept this means that glucose channels do not open.)	2
8.	(a)	(i)	Encoding	1
		(ii)	Short-term memory has a limited capacity/span/stores only 5—9 pieces of information. (Accept any number between 5 and 9.)	1
		(iii)	Information can put into categories/related groups. **OR** Information can have detail/meaning added to it.	1
		(iv)	These trigger memories relating to the circumstances/conditions/environment/stimuli present when the memory was formed. **OR** Suitable example described.	1
	(b)		Cerebrum/cerebral cortex	1
9.	(a)	(i)	It/cars/objects which are further away look/appear/are smaller. **OR** It/cars/objects which are nearer look/appear/are bigger.	1
		(ii)	The view of cars/objects which are further away is (partially) blocked/screened/obstructed/covered by nearer cars/objects.	1
	(b)		Binocular disparity	1
	(c)	(i)	16	1

Question			Expected response	Max Mark
		(ii)	To prevent them learning the position of the coin. OR To prevent them remembering where the coin was. OR To make sure that the experiment/results were valid.	1
		(iii)	The (student's) left eye is better/more accurate at <u>judging distance</u>. OR The (student's) right eye is worse/less accurate at <u>judging distance</u>.	1
10.	(a)	(i)	1. Less/a lower number/a lower percentage of females smoke than males in <u>all age groups</u>. OR More/a higher number/a higher percentage of males smoke than females in <u>all age groups</u>. 2. The percentage/number of female smokers decreases with age. 3. The percentage/number of male smokers increases to 25–34 years <u>and</u> then decreases. *Any 2 for 2 marks*	2
		(ii)	Many <u>older smokers</u> have died (from smoking related illnesses). (Accept 65+ as older.)	1
	(b)	(i)	Nicotine binds to <u>acetylcholine</u> receptors. OR Nicotine mimics the action of <u>acetylcholine</u>.	1
		(ii)	Dopamine induces feelings of pleasure/euphoria/makes them feel good. OR Dopamine stimulates/activates/triggers the reward pathway.	1
		(iii)	It causes a decrease in the number/sensitivity of <u>receptors</u>.	1
	(c)		Individuals <u>identify</u> with the celebrity and stop smoking/change their behaviour/change their beliefs to be like them/as they admire them.	1
	(d)		43 000	1
11.	(a)	(i)	There were a high/higher number of cases in 1991 and 1992/two years.	1
		(ii)	Endemic	1
		(iii)	The cases would not occur every year/regularly/constantly. OR The cases would occur occasionally/randomly/irregularly/less frequently.	1
	(b)	(i)	Individuals who had not been immunised were unlikely to come into contact with infected individuals.	1

Question			Expected response	Max Mark
		(ii)	Due to malnutrition/poverty/rejection by some of the population/lack of education/lack of access to medical resources or vaccines/geographical remoteness.	1
12.	(a)	(i)	Epithelial/epithelium.	1
		(ii)	They produce secretions/chemicals/mucus/sweat/stomach acid/tears/sebum.	1
	(b)		Chemical: histamine (1) Explanation: causes vasodilation/increases capillary permeability (1)	2
	(c)	(i)	Phagocyte: engulfs it/ingests it/takes it in <u>and</u> digests it/breaks it down. (1) NK cell: induces/triggers apoptosis of (infected) <u>cell</u> OR induces/triggers production of self-destructive enzymes/self-destruction/programmed <u>cell</u> death (in the infected <u>cell</u>). (1)	2
		(ii)	They release/produce <u>cytokines</u>.	1
13.	A		1. At puberty a (releaser) hormone is produced by the hypothalamus. 2. The pituitary gland releases follicle stimulating hormone/FSH <u>and</u> interstitial cell stimulating hormone/ICSH. 3. FSH/ICSH acts on/targets the testes. 4. FSH stimulates sperm production in the seminiferous tubules. 5. ICSH stimulates the production of testosterone in the interstitial cells. 6. Testosterone stimulates sperm production. 7. Sperm/gametes are produced from germline cells by meiosis. 8. Testosterone activates the prostate gland/seminal vesicles. 9. Secretions affect/maintain sperm mobility/viability **or** named example 10. Negative feedback control/feedback inhibition of sperm/testosterone production exists. 11. High levels of testosterone inhibits/reduces/controls FSH/ICSH production. (Accept LH in place of ICSH for point 2 only.) *Any 8 for 8 marks*	8

Question			Expected response	Max Mark
	B		1. Drug treatment/fertility drugs are used to stimulate/trigger ovulation/ super ovulation.	8
			2. (Some) drugs prevent the negative feedback of oestrogen on FSH production.	
			3. Other drugs mimic the effect of FSH/LH.	
			4. Artificial Insemination is used if a man has a low sperm count.	
			5. (Several) sperm/semen samples are collected. **OR** Sperm can be provided by a donor.	
			6. Sperm/semen is inserted into the female reproductive tract by means other than sexual intercourse/syringe.	
			7. Intra-cytoplasmic sperm injection/ ICSI is used when man has a low sperm count/when sperm are defective.	
			8. The <u>head</u> of the sperm is (directly) injected/inserted into the egg.	
			9. During In vitro fertilisation/IVF eggs are fertilised outside the body.	
			10. Zygotes/fertilised eggs are incubated. **OR** Blastocysts/balls of cells/embryos are transferred into the uterus/ womb.	
			11. Pre-implantation genetic diagnosis/ PGD identifies genetic disorders/ chromosome abnormalities.	
			Any 8 for 8 marks	

HIGHER HUMAN BIOLOGY
2018 SPECIMEN QUESTION PAPER

PAPER 1

Question	Answer	Mark
1.	D	1
2.	C	1
3.	A	1
4.	D	1
5.	A	1
6.	C	1
7.	B	1
8.	B	1
9.	B	1
10.	A	1
11.	A	1
12.	C	1
13.	A	1
14.	B	1
15.	A	1

Question	Answer	Mark
16.	D	1
17.	C	1
18.	B	1
19.	C	1
20.	D	1
21.	D	1
22.	C	1
23.	D	1
24.	B	1
25.	B	1

PAPER 2

Question			Expected response	Max Mark
1.	(a)		Process — Differentiation Explanation — Only the genes for producing proteins (characteristic) for that type of cell are expressed/switched on.	2
	(b)		First division — Homologous chromosomes are separated. Second division — Chromatids are separated.	2
	(c)		That embryos are destroyed in order to obtain stem cells. (Accept that doing this may be safer than using the drug directly on humans/ trial subjects. **OR** Accept that people suffering from the disease will be delayed getting/deprived of a potential treatment. **OR** Accept that embryonic stem cells may be used in place of animals.)	1
2.	(a)		RNA polymerase	1
	(b)		Ribosome	1
	(c)	(i)	Only one gene is transcribed/forms mRNA. **OR** The primary mRNA only codes for one protein.	1
		(ii)	Introns/non coding regions of genes are removed (in RNA splicing). **OR** The mature mRNA transcript only contains exons/coding regions of genes.	1
3.	(a)		41 (Accept — 54 to 95.)	1
	(b)		Amplification/replication/copying of DNA.	1
	(c)		Separation of the (DNA) strands. **OR** Breaking of hydrogen bonds between the (DNA) strands.	1
	(d)		They bind/anneal/join to (the ends of) target/complementary sequences of the DNA (being copied).	1

Question			Expected response	Max Mark
	(e)		To provide an optimum/better temperature for DNA polymerase.	1
	(f)		640	1
4.	(a)		Axes have correct scales and labels. (1) Points correctly plotted and line drawn. (1)	2
	(b)	(i)	Volume of urea solution. OR Volume of urease solution. OR Concentration of urease solution. OR Volume/length of agar/diameter of test tube. OR Volume/concentration of indicator in agar.	1
		(ii)	Temperature of the tube contents/test tubes.	1
	(c)		The experiment was repeated at each urea concentration. OR The experiment was repeated and averages calculated.	1
	(d)		To allow time for the ammonia to (fully) diffuse/spread through the agar/jelly.	1
	(e)		As the urea/substrate concentration increased more ammonia/end-product was produced. OR As the urea/substrate concentration decreased less ammonia/end-product was produced.	1
	(f)		48	1
	(g)	(i)	The inhibitor/thiourea blocked the active site on the urease/enzyme.	1
		(ii)	Not all active sites were blocked. OR Some active sites were still available.	1
5.	(a)		Energy investment — ATP molecules are broken down/used up (to provide energy). OR Phosphorylation/addition of phosphate to glucose/intermediates occurs. (1) Energy pay-off — ATP molecules are produced. (1)	2
	(b)		Name — acetyl (group)/acetyl coenzyme A/acetyl CoA. (1) Conditions — when oxygen is present/in aerobic conditions. (1) OR Name — lactate/lactic acid. (1) Conditions — when oxygen is absent.OR Insufficient/in anaerobic conditions. (1)	2

Question			Expected response	Max Mark
	(c)		Slow twitch — from aerobic respiration/ the electron transport chain/ATP synthase. (1) Fast twitch — glycogen. (1)	2
6.	(a)		SS	1
	(b)		50	1
	(c)	(i)	It alters the (DNA) nucleotide sequence. OR It replaces one nucleotide with another.	1
		(ii)	An incorrect amino acid is placed in the protein/polypeptide/haemoglobin. OR One amino acid is replaced by another in the protein/polypeptide/ haemoglobin. OR The amino acid sequence/protein becomes shorter (due to a stop codon).	1
	(d)		Pre-implantation genetic diagnosis/PGD.	1
	(e)		This drug could switch on the gene for fetal haemoglobin (in the child so haemoglobin is produced). OR This drug could stop the gene for fetal haemoglobin being switched off (in the child so haemoglobin is produced).	1
7.	(a)	(i)	55	1
		(ii)	The pituitary gland releases follicle stimulating hormone/FSH. (1) FSH stimulates the follicle/ovary to release oestrogen. (1)	2
	(b)		300	1
	(c)		The corpus luteum has started to degenerate/break down so it produces less progesterone.	1
	(d)		They prevent the negative feedback effect of oestrogen on FSH secretion. OR They mimic the action of FSH/LH.	1
8.	(a)		The endothelium.	1
	(b)		It can contract/vasoconstrict to reduce blood flow (to some areas). OR It can relax/vasodilate to increase blood flow (to some areas).	1

Question			Expected response	Max Mark
	(c)		<u>Formation</u>	5
			1. The atheroma can rupture damaging the endothelium/layer X.	
			2. Clotting factors are released.	
			3. Prothrombin is converted/changed/ activated into thrombin.	
			4. Fibrinogen is converted into fibrin (by thrombin).	
			5. Fibrin/threads form a meshwork that seals the wound/clots the blood.	
			<u>Effects</u>	
			6. The clot/thrombus formed may break loose, forming an embolus.	
			7. A clot/thrombus may lead to a heart attack/stroke.	
			At least one point from each area for 5 marks.	
9.	(a)	(i)	98 beats/minute	1
		(ii)	Stroke volume increased as oxygen uptake increased, until 2 litres/min, after which it remained constant.	1
		(iii)	150	1
	(b)		18·72	1
	(c)	(i)	It represents systolic blood pressure. OR It is when blood is surging/being pumped through the arteries. OR It is when the artery wall is stretched.	1
		(ii)	High blood pressure forces (more) fluid out of the capillaries. (1) Lymph vessels cannot reabsorb all the excess (tissue) fluid. (1)	2
10.	(a)	(i)	Their blood glucose concentration starts to decrease after 30 minutes. OR Their blood glucose concentration returns to normal after 60 minutes. OR Their blood glucose concentration increases at a slower rate/to a lower level/for a shorter time compared to individual A.	1
		(ii)	Between 0 and 60 minutes blood glucose concentration increased and then it decreased between 60 and 150 minutes. (1) It increased from 4·8 m mol/litre to 11·2 m mol/litre/by 6·4 m mol/litre. OR It decreased from 11·2 m mol/litre to 7·6 m mol/litre/by 3·6 m mol litre. (1) (Accept it increases up to 60 minutes and then decreases.)	2

Question			Expected response	Max Mark
	(b)		Type 1 — Insulin is not produced (so blood glucose concentration cannot be controlled). (1) Type 2 — Cells are less sensitive to insulin/have fewer insulin receptors/ have developed insulin resistance. (1)	2
11.	(a)	(i)	1. As age increases, the frequency/ number of cases of obesity increases. (1) 2. The frequency/number of cases is always higher in 2012 (compared to 2003). (1)	2
		(ii)	1·536 million/ 1 536 000	1
	(b)		Reduce their intake of fats/sugars/ carbohydrates. OR Take more exercise/become more active.	1
12.	(a)		1. Use people of similar ages/have a similar age range (in each group). (1) 2. Use people of the same gender/have a similar gender balance (in each group). (1) (Accept — use people of similar memory ability in each group.)	2
	(b)		To prevent rehearsal of the words keeping them in short-term memory. OR To remove the words from short-term memory. OR To make sure that any words recalled had come from long-term memory.	1
	(c)		Lists are easier to recall (from long-term memory) if the words do not have a similar/have a different meaning. OR Lists are harder to recall (from long-term memory) if the words have a similar meaning/do not have a different meaning.	1
13.	(a)		Cell P has membrane receptors that are specific to the polio virus/antigens on the virus.	1
	(b)		B lymphocyte	1
	(c)		They quickly respond to another attack by the same virus/pathogen so preventing infection. OR They produce specific lymphocytes that destroy the virus/pathogen before the individual shows symptoms.	1
	(d)		The polio and influenza viruses have different antigens.	1
	(e)		Neither the subjects nor the researchers know whether the subject is getting the vaccine or the placebo.	1

Question			Expected response	Max Mark
14.	(a)	(i)	1955/1956	1
		(ii)	Decrease in vaccination rate/lack of vaccines available. **OR** Mass immigration. **OR** Mutation of the whooping cough bacteria. **OR** Adverse publicity about the vaccine.	1
	(b)		A large percentage of the population has been immunised. **(1)** This means that there is a very low chance that non-immune individuals will come into contact with infected individuals. **(1)**	2
15.	(a)		Shorter life span/lower survival rate, so no time to develop heart disease.	1
	(b)	(i)	20	1
		(ii)	300 000	1
	(c)		Widespread vaccination might not be possible due to the effects of poverty. Accept Widespread vaccination might not be possible due to rejection by some of the population/lack of education/ malnutrition. **OR** Widespread vaccination might not be possible due to lack of access to doctors/nurses/medical resources/ vaccines/geographical remoteness.	1
16.	(a)	(i)	1986—1991	1
		(ii)	Cases of pulmonary TB decreased while cases of non-pulmonary TB increased.	1
		(iii)	11 : 5	1
	(b)		HIV attacks/destroys T lymphocytes weakening the immune system/reducing the ability of the body to respond to the infection.	1
17.	A		1. The autonomic nervous system (ANS) works automatically/without conscious control. 2. It is controlled by the medulla (region of the brain). 3. It is made up of sympathetic and parasympathetic systems. 4. These two systems are antagonistic in action. 5. The SAN/sino-atrial node controls heart rate.	8

Question			Expected response	Max Mark
			6. The sympathetic system speeds up the heart rate/impulses leaving the SAN. 7. by releasing noradrenaline. 8. The parasympathetic system slows down the heart rate/impulses leaving the SAN. 9. by releasing acetylcholine. 10. The parasympathetic system increases the rate of peristalsis while the sympathetic system decreases it. 11. The parasympathetic system increases the rate of intestinal secretions while the sympathetic system decreases it. *Any 8 for 8 marks.*	
	B		1. Neurotransmitters relay/carry messages from nerve to nerve/ muscle. 2. The gap between nerves/nerves and muscles is called the synaptic cleft. 3. Neurotransmitters are stored in vesicles. 4. Arrival of an impulse causes vesicles to fuse with the (presynaptic) membrane and release their contents/neurotransmitter (molecules). 5. Neurotransmitters diffuse across the cleft/gap/synapse. 6. Neurotransmitters bind to receptors. 7. A minimum number/threshold of neurotransmitter molecules must attach to receptors to trigger an impulse. 8. Receptors determine whether the signal is excitatory or inhibitory. 9. Neurotransmitters are removed by enzymes/reuptake. 10. Removal prevents continuous stimulation of the postsynaptic neurons. 11. Summation of weak stimuli can release enough neurotransmitter to trigger an impulse. *Any 8 for 8 marks.*	8

Acknowledgements

Permission has been sought from all relevant copyright holders and Hodder Gibson is grateful for the use of the following:

Image © kurhan/stock.adobe.com (2017 Section 2 page 15);
Image © Tupungato/Shutterstock.com (2018 Section 2 page 17).